THE MURDI
BILL'S O' JACK'S

Foreword

Saddleworth, a widespreading district in the West Pennines in the south of what was once called the West Riding, derives its name from one of the moorland hills which slopes easily down to the Lancashire border, and which is perfectly saddle-shaped.

Many villages compose the district; villages of dark millstone cottages mainly, following the lines of the valleys spreading fanwise into the high moors. Their brown and black millstone is that of the high peaks, jagged pinnacles far off, thrusting into the sky, and the cottages seem merely an orderly rearrangement of those rocks and crags.

The moors, seen at a distance from the high roads, are as velvet; green and gold and brown, of grass and bracken and ling and the reddish-purple of heather. They are serene enough, amiable a little in the summer months for the grouse-shooter and the lone climbers of the black crags. They are majestic moors, onetime and only-ever English home of the golden eagle, and for it a fitting home; sometimes described as "smiling" but it is a thin smile, of little warmth even in summer; a smile down-curving in a hard winter to a menacing snarl. Men and women have died here of sheer exposure: in a fairly recent winter a storm had reached the fury and ferocity of a blizzard, a swirling fog of whiteness – not the hushed softness of yellow humid fog but a maniacally-howling, ripping and tearing, blinding whiteness. In the storm a snow-trapped car, its heater-system finally exhausted, had to admit the moorland winter and the young couple within, in each other's arms for a little last warmth, had to admit it too... and they died: died within a mile or two of the Transpennine Motorway, highest, possibly the wildest, in Europe, the one that "never closes". North to north-west a few miles are the "Wuthering Heights".

The nearest village to the high black crags is that of Greenfield; so pleasantly named, yet so intimately associated with the most vile, and the most bloody, of crimes in English legal history; the "Moors Murders" are surely the most vile, and the murder above Greenfield at the lonely Moorcock Inn known as "Bill's o' Jack's" was literally the most bloody, quite simply in sheer avoirdupois weight of blood shed.

Personified, the moors and their remote, aloof peaks have the same dual nature as man: pleasing, tranquil, loving and deeply loved; hateful, ferocious, merciless, with treachery in mind and murder in heart. And disaster, tragedy and mysterious

3

murder have haunted pleasant Greenfield, so quiet and unpretentious; of all the moorland villages the most closely tucked in intimately tucked in, to the awesome, lowering moors and forced to share their terrible history, and their stories...

Nearing the nineteenth century Robert Bradbury, or as he was named in the local manner "Robert o' Pears", farmer at Waterside near Greenfield, employed a housekeeper, conventionally so-called. Children were born to them who, after a few years when they might reasonably have been held old enough to go elsewhere, were deemed to have done so, since they were no longer seen. Legend has it that Robert was observed on various occasions digging, by day and by night, although knowledgeable observers could not see this as having any bearing on the work of the farm. At last the "housekeeper" too, last seen walking the remotest hillside with Robert, disappeared. She is, a long-standing ghost story goes, the "woman wearing grey cloak" who walks the lonely, half-hidden lane below the mill on the far hillside. Later tenants of the farm spoke also of ghostly children walking the house, never speaking.

This still-persisting story seems to confuse the mysteriously-vanished, spectral children with the very real discovery of the cadavers and skeletons of children mass-buried in the vicinity. These were exhumed and taken to nearby Boarshurst for re-burial. Hundreds waited for and witnessed the sad procession. The bodies were held to be those of pauper children who had lived and died at "Forty Row", a row of twenty back-to-back cottages which made forty tiny dwellings.

These were mere dormitories for the mills. The pauper-children workers had been brought from the south, from poor-law hospitals, jetsam of the port slums, simply abandoned; many were of prison birth, many just unwanted idiots. At last finding a single-brick-wall "dormitory home" in the cold box-cottages of Forty Row, they briefly lived there, uneasy, hungry and soon worked to death in the local mills. One such mill was Brun Clough, later described as a black, evil-looking ruin, where children were heard screaming on wild dark nights in winter. Another mill was grimly named "Limbo". And the stories of these and others like them run more and more thinly with the years, becoming now as tenuous as the "Grey Lady" ghost and as unreal - but the bodies and the burial ground are real enough.

James Platt, a schoolmaster, was present at the re-burial and he authenticates it. He authenticates too another burial, and this account is likely to last longer than penned words since it is in simple verses chiselled in stone; they are inscribed on a huge gravestone flat on the ground in the south-west corner of the graveyard across the lane from Saddleworth Church:

HERE
lie the dreadfully bruised and lacerated bodies of William Bradbury and Thomas, his son, both of Greenfield, who were together savagely murdered in an unusually horrid manner, on Monday night, April 2nd. 1832, William being 84, and Thomas 46 years old.

4

"Throughout the land wherever news is read,
Intelligence of their sad end has spread,
Those now who talk of far-famed Greenfield hills,
Will think of Bill o' Jack's and Tom o' Bill's.

Such interest did their tragic end excite,
That, ere they were removed from human sight,
Thousands on thousands came to see,
The bloody scene of the catastrophy,

One house, one business, and one bed,
And one most shocking death they had,
One funeral came, one inquest past,
And now one grave they have at last."

****

James Platt, MP and a member of a world-famous engineering firm, was accidentally killed, shot by his brother-in-law, while with a shooting party on a neighbouring moor. Ashway Gap, a blackstone shooting lodge at Greenfield, was his home.

****

In 1949 the moors themselves inflicted death directly – at Indian's Head, an outthrust from the high moor of jagged black fangs of rocks, seen from away over the valley floor to be like the aquiline features of the befeathered head of an Indian brave. On this particular day mist had, as often, shrouded the high peaks so that the jagged rocks were as the rocks of the shoreline, below the surface... the aircraft sailing in that mist-sea struck, and many died.

Disaster persisted: one of the survivors was a three-year-old infant who, years later as a schoolboy, was killed in a railway accident.

****

Twentieth-century newspaper headlines speak for themselves. First, the "Moors Murders":

Oldham Evening Chronicle, 19th October 1965: " 'Moor squad' enlist old science. Copper divining rods....searching Saddleworth Moors for graves...Graves hunt goes on... A biting east wind spurred overalled men... dug deeper to discover the remains of other missing children."

Oldham Evening Chronicle, 21st October 1965: "Body is unearthed.. Police Officers digging on Saddleworth Moor exhumed a body, this afternoon, close to the Greenfield-Holmfirth Road; three and a half miles out of Greenfield."

Another particularly bloody case involved an eighteen-year-old girl:

Oldham Evening Chronicle, 25th October 1979: "Tip-off leads Police to body in Grave... two men and an eighteen-year-old girl have been charged with the murder of a twenty-two-year-old Scotsman, of no fixed abode, following the discovery, in a shallow moorland grave, of a body bearing severe injuries."

Oldham Evening Chronicle, 31st October 1979: "Girl, 18, dug grave with bare hands."

5

Oldham Evening Chronicle, 21st November 1979: "Axe and machete. Picnic site death case 'jigsaw' ready."

Oldham Evening Chronicle, 16th May 1980: "Axe killers get life."

* * * * * * * * * *

The murders at Bill's o' Jack's Inn   April 1832

The following narrative is part-conjecture, part-fact; the conjecture based on the rumours and the theories current at the time among the villagers of Saddleworth, who were much more searching in their examination of the evidence than was the inquest, which was remarkably cursory.

An almost incredible feature of these murders is that one of the victims, William Bradbury, when asked as he lay dying if he could name his attackers, was able to answer, but because of dreadfully severe mouth and facial injuries, his words were an almost unintelligible slurred mutter: "Pats", or "Platt", or "Platters", any one of which was – astonishing coincidence – applicable to possible perpetrators of the crimes.

Yet the murder remained unsolved; and although a reward, finally £200, was offered for information leading to a prosecution, no semblance of a case could be mounted against anyone. The murder remains unsolved in spite of evidence of a "confession" that turned up thirty years late, and which became disclosed to general knowledge nearly a hundred and thirty years later still.

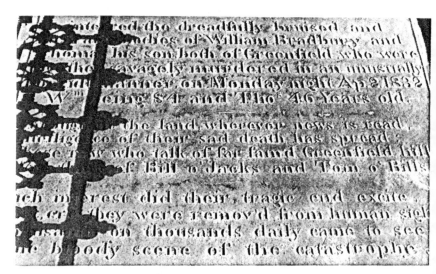

Gravestone in the churchyard of St Chad's, Saddleworth, bearing James Platt's verses.

6

Chapter 1

The small moorland village square, held in the right angle made by the church and the inn, was brilliant with white-gold sunlight, and the whole of it was filled with stalls of an early Ribbon Fair, the "fairings stalls" holding ribbons and frills and furbelows, bright for feminine whimsy and offered with abrupt shyness by taciturn young men, gallant for the day. These stalls were few. More stalls, solid platforms of legs and with white-sheeted tops, lined both sides of every approach lane. There was crockery of all colours and sizes; pans and dishes vast enough for armies (and armies there were, armies of children, on most moorland farms) mingled with knives, hatchets, screws, short axes, hammers and tools, ropes, nails – enough to suggest that the farms were to be screwed and nailed to their precarious lodging on the mountain sides. Food stalls were crowded to their edges with the produce of many a hard-toiling dairy farm... anything and everything.

The crowd was packed shoulder to shoulder too. A few, mill-workers, spinners and weavers, were in fustian; but most were farm-workers and farmers, heavily whiskered below wide-brimmed straw hats, masculinity oddly emphasised by the womanish, smocked, gown-like over-shirts they wore. The women were in the main as sturdy and broad in the shoulder as their men, and mostly plain of dress and of looks but attractive, being full-figured, high-busted and of bonny complexion; and this pleasing crowd moved in ceaseless slow minuet, as it were, to the jingling music of a street organ.

In a small corner where the main lane entered the square a girl, not of these parts, stood offering from a basket plaited ribbons and rosettes. She was a "burnplatter", a plaiter of baskets, a maker of besoms and brooms from the rushes and osiers of moors and hill-streams; a gypsy of the encampment on the far wild Wessenden Moor; and she attracted the sidelong glances of the men, and the hostile stares of the shrewd women parading by. The girl had beauty, dark and large-eyed, oddly accentuated by tangled, somewhat unkempt, tightly curled hair framing a face none too clean. Her loose bodice, an affront to the tightly-laced village women, was even more loosely laced to show a perfect line of cleavage. Her skirt, patched and uneven of hem, was impud-ently high over bare dusty feet and neat ankles bared enough to show the beginnings of shapely calves. But it was a frank sensuality in every line of her that gave vividness to her and made all, willingly or unwillingly, aware of her.

But there was a moment when all glances, the girl's particularly, turned elsewhere - to the head of the lane some hundred yards away where a man, seemingly known to most, had entered. In this crystal light the moors at his back, rolling and curving miles into the far south, appeared as light brown velvet, scrabbled with green and seemed near, larger than life. And the man looming there at the head of the lane seemed larger than life too.

He was over six feet in height, straight, and so broad of shoulder as to belie his towering stature. His legs were athletic, long, those of a distance-runner; which indeed he sometimes was in his function of moorland gamekeeper. He had an aggressive strut to his walk, that of a born fighter, but stature and movement were not, alone, the main cause of the crowd's and the girl's attention. As he neared his features became marked: his hair was sandy-red, bunched a little at the forehead like a bull's; he had the coarse skin of the lecher, his eyes were hooded and perpetually lustful, a little upslanted at the outer corners. He looked, and was, a giant satyr, red as the devil, face flushed and glinting with red bristles almost up to the eyes.

He approached to within six feet of the ribbon-girl, then stopped to face her, not speaking; there was little need to speak what was in his mind. If he had quivered and snorted like a stallion he could not have more explicitly declared his lust, intense, frank and animal-like and, so, unselfconscious of the curious knowing glances of the passers-by. And the girl, perfectly aware of it and with a hate as evident, perhaps because of the violent repulsion of like for like, spat copiously and noisily in front of him.

There was a snigger of laughter from a small part of the crowd, almost halted to watch the vivid little play, and the man whipped round to face them. A glare was enough, and slightly apprehensive swains hurried away their giggling wenches; the gamekeeper, Tom Bradbury, was well known to be quick with his fists, too.

A snigger again, this time from the left and Bradbury whipped round again upon the sound. A youngish man, slight and twisted of frame, was seated on the low drystone wall across the road and he had observed to himself, with a half-smile and some resignation Tom's hunched shoulders, sure sign in him of resentment or of rage.

"Tom's in lumber again," he registered, and his eyes were wary over the smile: eyes showing only half of bulging, pale, rat-like orbs, albino and like the rat's showing cunning but no fear; his pointed chin was in no way weak.

As Tom approached, an imperative flick of his head jerked the other to his feet, to walk gracefully and light-footedly alongside him striding into the lanes of the fair and across to the inn. They spoke not a word crossing the tiny church square, nor again in the inn over pints of ale: Tom dourly silent, the other, Eliphalet o' John's, perforce silent so as not to be ahead of the leader.

The inn was fair-happy, jocular... half a day through and the drinkers half-taken with ale. Leather rings slapped on the ring-board, dominoes clicked and the "fifteens" of cribbage were cheerily shouted over cards thumped down heartily. Ale at length loosened Tom's tongue. "I've given them bloody platters up on my land a good puncing round," he said grimly, in a tightened voice. Eliphalet involuntarily glanced down at Tom's thick boots as if to look for evidence of "puncing", that form of fighting which usually smeared the bootcaps with blood. "No," said Tom, impatiently but more good-humouredly, "not real puncing; length of my tongue, like. I'm not getting down to fighting all of them, even on my land."

8

Eliphalet noted the "my land", repeated, and was careful not to allow a bubble of mirth to surface. "Which land, Tom?" he asked solemnly.

"Wessenden Head. Not a bloody penny rent have they given me."

"Nor need they," but Eliphalet said that only in the silence of his innermost mind.

The brief exchange released Tom into a better humour: "Let's look into the fair."

While they paced the fair, Eliphalet from time to time produced a small, squared, bright-blue bottle - a gin bottle but filled with local spirit - and they shared swigs at this, Tom first. The crude alcohol seemed to dissolve Tom's dourness and to replace it with an equally crude excitement: Eliphalet noted, silently as always, Tom's constant manoeuvring to look down the stall-lanes to where the platter-girl had stood; but she was not to be seen. Finally Tom seemed to become weary of the fair. "Naught doing here," he said. "There's a bull-baiting down at the Shaw Brook. Let's go to that."

Theirs was a slightly erratic course, the three or so miles to the baiting: a number of stops with women, some just young wenches, of whom Tom appeared to know many and Eliphalet none; or at least none regarded him as he smiled thinly at the crude bawdy banter and the screams of mock-outrage that went for passing conversation. So that the two were late for the "setting on" of two brindle bull-terriers and a half-bred dog to a strong black young bull. This was tethered in the middle of a wide, slowly-running pebbly brook, upon the waters of which, at a distance, appeared to be streaming long red ribbons. The banks of the brook were crowded with men and women and a few boys, and on a low hump-backed bridge a little way upstream bunched another, better-advantaged group - the dog owners and a few cronies claiming this privileged place.

Shouts, pierced by the screaming calls of women, rose in crescendo as the weakened bull began to stagger, faltering on the shifting pebbles. Down he went, the dogs were instantly at his throat and blood began to flow mightily. But now the dogs began to falter, drained for a few moments by their own fury, and they fell back. The bull, still down in the water, turned his head to lick his wounds; and this stirred the half-breed dog to attack again, biting savagely at the soft muzzle until teeth met and held. A great bellowing by the bull sprang the other dogs into action and men joined in, wading through the water swinging cudgels and staves. The almost-screaming dogs were blood-crazed, but the men were beyond blood-craze, they were money-crazed too. For the bull was holding on; his wounds, though hideous, were superficial and time was running out - the wagers were on the time taken to kill. It was the bettors of "short time", ignoring the howls of those for whom time was winning, who waded in and laid their heavy cudgels to the bull's head, flanks and vulnerable exposed belly.

Tom and Eliphalet chuckled merrily, but not for long. The action of the baiting soon ended as the beast, too far gone to raise his head, could no longer keep his muzzle clear of the stream. And so mercifully he drowned.

9

"Come on, Eli," commanded Tom. "All o'er. We saw the best of it," and he turned upon the words and nearly cannoned into a man, not of moorland dress or appearance but who must have been standing watching near enough to hear Tom's words, for he said, "Yes. Thank God it's over," almost as if in answer.

"What's the matter, mister?" Tom asked sneeringly. "Sight of blood upset ye? Turned ye woman-like?"

It was meant to be provocative but the man showed no resentment, indeed spoke again slowly and reflectively and almost as if he had not heard: "What sort of men are they?" but he seemed to ask that of himself. Then he repeated his rhetorical question, but this time looking so directly into Tom's eyes that Eli shifted a little out of range. But Tom did not respond, merely looked a little puzzled; and the man moved off. threading a path through the crowd now streaming away, still arguing, still quarrelling, exchanging a blow here and there, still intent on the baiting.

Only one or two spared a glance for the man moving against the flow of people and holding against his mouth a brilliant red silk neckerchief; holding it as if against a noisome smell, or possibly as if he had no wish to have his face seen.

Chapter 2

The stir and excitement of the fair, the exhilaration of the bull-baiting and the evening dancing and merry-making in the inns seemed to carry over into the Sunday, and even the Moorcock Inn some way up the moorside was thronged by mid-morning. The inn had once been Jack Bradbury's, was now his son Bill's and was best known as "Bill's o' Jack's". There was a great circle of spindle-back chairs before the blazing fire in the massive wide hearth, and all were full. Lawyer, butcher, labourer, farmer, carter and shopman sat in close once-a-week companionship, pint pots and tankards already "well seasoned" and pipe smoke blued a little the sun-bright, plain, bare-wood taproom. The rest of the space and the other smaller rooms were a-bustle, heavy-booted footfalls "crinkling" on the newly-sanded floors. And Tom Bradbury worked quietly and well for his father, serving ale from a huge wooden tray that only a strong man could have handled so dexterously and kept so quickly replenished of its pots. Most, though, served themselves, a bantering, shifting crowd that gave Tom a good deal more impudence than they might have done out in the lane.

"How come so quiet-like, Tom?" asked one. "Belly-ache from last night's ale?"

"Not be Tom's belly that'll be aching after a Saturday night," another responded, as if for Tom.

"Bit lower down," said another – but Tom did not rise to the guffaws, not all of them good-humoured and he followed his work, unusually quiet, even aware of it himself, for commonly he would have kept the banter down to a very respectful level indeed. But not so today.

With the chiming of noon there began an oddly quick exodus. Most were on their way within minutes, men streaming through the great, square, roughhewn-lintelled doorway and ale-jocund, blinking a little in the thin sunshine already westering, making haste to Sunday dinner and to wives hot from the oven-cooking and a mite short in temper; some wives were quick to use the rolling pin or the baking paddle! The bustling, loud-talking crowd of the inn was quickly out and away, bachelors and wife-free soon going too as the cheerful morning atmosphere of companionship ended; and quietness was left in the rooms, only blue smoke and the strong smell of ale lingering now. Bill accompanied the last and slowest drinker to the door and there raised his hand in signal to a cottage far along the lane, up the moor a way.

Very shortly a little familiar procession left the cottage for the inn: James Whitehead and his wife, and a young girl about twelve years old. James bore a great black iron pan of boiled potatoes and a smaller pan of boiled cabbage; his wife carried a square roasting tin with a vast round of beef and roast potatoes; and the little girl, stepping carefully, somewhat gingerly carried a jug of gravy. The food was covered with snowy cloths and carefully delivered to the square, bare table in the back kitchen. All was done with nicety and tidiness, the hornhandled knives and forks precisely laid, for Bill loved his Sunday dinner just so and put his hand deep in his pocket for the settling and the paying for it. The little girl was his granddaughter, Mary Winterbottom, who helped the Whiteheads on Sundays and who looked forward to her second spending penny, and Bill paid this over with a kind old-man's smile, patient and fond, sparing a minute or two for the child's chatter. "There's tha penny, my love," he said after a little teasing and they departed, Tom sitting silent and expressionless waiting for them to go.

As they went Mary, clutching the penny in her pinafore pocket gaily said, "Penny for the morning, Mrs Whitehead."

"Lucky Mary. More than I got in a fourweeks. Don't spend it all in one shop."

"That I shan't. I spread it out," Mary promised and then, "Uncle Tom ne'er gives me anything, and I bet he has as much."

"Tha'rt too young a lass," said Mrs Whitehead, drily and cryptically; though her husband James understood and grinned a little.

Dinner for the two men was mainly an affair of silence. Any civilities would have been an embarrassment to both and they took their own food on to the plate, each with a short carving knife cutting great slices, eaten from the point of the knife. Tall blue quart mugs of ale seemed to act as gauges, for when they were emptied the meal was finished. Then Tom took the two jugs in hand and looked across at his father, who nodded, and Tom went off to the cellar to their special barrel. He returned with the jugs to the taproom where each settled, quart in hand, in a grandfather spindleback before a fire still large. Occasionally there was a word or so, curt, brusque, somewhat forbidding on Tom's part, and there was only a rough familiarity of many years between father and son. They were comfortable enough in each other's company, no more; and they soon fell into complete silence. Quietness, warmth and strong ale brought on drowsiness, and Bill at length put his jug down on the floor at his side, slid down a little in his chair and within moments was snoring. Minutes later Tom joined him in sleep, but his was uneasy, whereas Bill hardly stirred on his hard-seated chair and seemed as if he might be settled until late. Tom fidgetted, slept awhile, then half-woke a number of times, until at length he woke to near full consciousness and a stirring in his body. This at length completely roused him; he sat for a few moments staring into the fire and pondering, then as softly as he might on the grating sand he left the taproom by the front door, leaving it, as always, unlocked.

In the quietness of Tom's departure there was little concern for his father's afternoon sleep, but more for secretiveness as he left on yet another of regular visits to a cottage on the lower slopes of "Pots and Pans". His secretiveness was misplaced; all the cottagers with a view of the slopes knew of Tom's visits to Madge's and tittle-tattle had spread the news abroad in the villages. So he might as well have walked in at her front door instead of going as he did through the tiny vegetable garden and the little back door, striding in familiarly.

Madge was near enough to plain, but her figure was good and filled out her simple frock and apron. Tom was pleased and gratified as she rose from a simple tea-meal, leaving it instantly and coming to put her hands on Tom's shoulders and look straight at him, smiling. That was all of her greeting; there was no dalliance, no kissing for civility nor affection, for this was needed by neither of them. Madge spoke one word, "Where?" but she knew the answer before it was made and Tom merely jerked a thumb: "Upstairs."

She turned at once to go, unfastening her apron and her frock-laces as she climbed the bare wooden stairs, while Tom took off his jacket to throw it across a chair, then followed her to the low-raftered, simply-furnished bedroom. Madge was a mite slow, a faint show of mock-modesty, Tom in no haste with the buttons and belt of his breeches; but this was as near as they came to a slight dalliance, a slight finesse. There was little of human grace and concern, it was soon ended for this time and after-courting was not wanted. They went downstairs in silence and there Tom, breeched and buttoned again, reached for his jacket to draw from the deep poacher pockets a brace of grouse, only a day or so illegally off the moor, and with them a stone bottle of ale. These he put on the table; and they were more, much more welcome to a poor widow-woman than any gewgaw token. With the gifts Tom achieved, as near as he could manage, a little joviality: "These 'uns thine. What the eye doesn't see..." he said and winked broadly. Then off and away, using the back door again; while Madge returned to the table as placidly as a served cow to its grazing.

Lower down the hillside, at a millhouse cottage there, a housewife called out to her husband: "Tom Bradbury's away, then,"she said, pointing. A tiny figure, black as a silhouette at the distance, was moving in and out of the black crags, seeming slow at the range but the husband said, "Making a fair pace, he is," from experience judging pace well. "Not many men, even i' these parts, could take Pots and Pans face at that speed, right after." "Well!" the wife rejoined. "He must be right fond and all o' walking, for that's not the quick way to the Moorcock."

Tom was indeed taking a new line and an arduous one, but straight across the moor and mountain-high of the Moorcock. Another impulse was pricking him on, one he could not rightly name but something of the sort that had sent him first striding south and westward, mountain-low, to Madge.

Soon, out of the crags, Tom took a lower line, off the high sky-line of the peaks and midway crossing the steepling slope the hard way - "one short leg" - but nearly invisible in green game-keeper jacket and buff breeches. The almost sheer sides of deeply-cut narrow ravines made hazardous his path, but this was the moor he knew and loved, as well he might with his own craggy nature... and he halted a few hardbreathing moments by one such ravine with a stream tumbling fast in the steepness, crystal-clear, speed-smoothed, its high-voiced sound lovely as a singing bird's. Yet the peace was almost instantly broken; a few feet across a stoat and a weasel, a rare encounter, met - each to refuse way. For a moment each was as frozen still then, too quick for the eye to register, the fight was joined: a whirling blood-spattering wheeling and lightning attack; ferocity locked with ferocity, ripping and tearing, with only tiny cries of rage, none of pain... until the weasel, the spirit of pure ferocity, began to prevail and the stoat, his relative in blood and courage and malignity, began to fail - not in spirit, but his body could do no more - and they parted just short of bloody murder.

As the stoat, low to ground, slunk away Tom, with the support of a bare wind-stripped bush at the bank edge, swung across to the tiny battleground. The weasel, recovering on the instant from blind exhaustion, limped away from him and Tom, although this was an enemy to him and to his game, took only a half-hearted kick, deliberately to miss. "Little sod!" he said admiringly with a half smile, but the smile quickly faded to give place to a scowling grimace. There it was again; that sense of a swinging in his head: a swaying, and a lostness for the moment, all in his head. He began his march again, impatiently striding, and he growled to himself aloud as men do in lonely hours on the moors, as dour with himself as with others: "Old man coming on," and he had felt it too, walking away from the bull-baiting. He knew in his deepest instincts that his words did not have the right sense - that it was something else - but he thrust thought away and tramped on, in full stride again.

After another half mile or so Tom began to make high ground again, until at last he was in sight of a tremendous panorama of flat moorland stretching away to far horizons and tiny townships. Away and to his left a mile or more was a smooth hillside and on it the blunt square mass of a moorland farmhouse and barns, long derelict and forlorn-seeming, but Tom took from his pocket a game-keeper's telescope: there were many figures moving in and around the grey buildings and smoke rose from the chimneys. Further along the hawthorn hedges ran up to outcropping black millstone, the ground below long since scooped out into caves, rough thatching and timbering at their entrances, equally rough male and female figures moving around them, too.

They were the "burnplatters" of Tom's Saturday ire: gypsy-like folk living by stealing and by telling fortunes at cottage doors; by making and selling a little illicit whisky; by making lucky tokens of the local heather for sale in the markets; by making besoms from the bog-rushes and the valley sallows; and, chiefest cause of Tom's anger, by hunting and poaching. They did not seem to be doing anything amiss just now and - Tom had to tell the truth to himself - nor had he come to look for that; he had given them until Monday, anyway. No, he had hoped to catch a glimpse of the girl, the ribbon-seller of the fair. But there was no-one to be distinguished at the distance and he had no wish for a closer acquaintance with the platters that day. He turned and departed, somewhat dispirited though he did not know why.

When he finally drew near to the Moorcock, this time by the main Yorkshire road and descending from the north, he saw that Eli was awaiting him. The inn was a few feet below road level, down the bank, and the main road was drystone-walled for some way past it; entrance to the inn was along a lane leading from a wide opening in the wall, gateless but having great square stone pillars. Eli was seated on the stone wall near to the gateway, facing the other way and Tom, who would normally have shinned over the wall to clamber down the bank, walked down the road towards him. Eli was a little surprised as Tom came down speaking to him from behind, and was not his usual tactful placatory self. "Why, Tom," he said, "I'd thought you'd have been coming up the road."

"And why do I have to be doing that?" Tom demanded.

"No, well," Eli hesitated, disconcerted, but Tom did not wish to press the point; he thought his Sunday afternoon visits were safe and so did not suspect the other of imputation.

"I've been nigh up to Wessenden Head," he said, "and I'm from there."

"Oh aye," Eli said, and waited.

Tom went on, "There were naught to take much notice on and I didn't draw nigh," and his attempt at casualness did not deceive Eli, who drew his man on by the simple expedient of being silent. "A lot on them," Tom mused on. "Couldn't rightly say from where I was - seemed more ner yesterday, ner before." A brief hesitation. "Can't say I could see the lass with the ribbon-tokens, tha knows. I've seen her the once, at some distance. Does she belong there, I wonder?"

"Aye," said Eli.

"How dost know, so sure like?" Tom demanded.

"I buys some of their whiskey. I wouldn't touch it, but I sells it on," Eli answered, "and I've been up there once or twice."

"Tha ne'er told me," Tom said.

"They're no friends o' thine, " Eli answered succinctly.

"Come along in," Tom commanded, " and I'll give thee a pint." Eli's comment was a discreetly silent one, "Tom wants summat", for Tom was not overly-generous.

Inside the inn Tom came quickly to the point and wanted to know
14

more of the girl. Had she a man up there? Relatives, brother, aught? How earned she a living? But only the last could Eli answer: "Mostly she sells tokens and lucky sprigs - tha knows, heather tied wi' a bit o' ribbon."

"Where does she sell?"

"Cottage doors; and at the roadside; and at fairs and suchlike, I reckon," Eli answered. "Oh, and down at Oldham, at the theatre door and at inn doors."

"Nights, then?"

"I reckon so. Likely works her way down by day."

"Isn't there a theatre tomorrow night?"

"Surely so."

Tom took Eli's pint pot from the bar and filled it to the top again. "Wouldst like to go?" he then asked.

"I've no money for that." Eli spoke decidedly.

"I'll pay."

Eli was now very intrigued. They said of Tom that he "had long pockets and short arms". "Count on me for sure," he said, and to himself, "Summat going on here."

Chapter 3

"Brandy-balls; brandy-balls,
Brandy and sugar.
Brandy-balls; brandy-balls,
Big as Saint Paul's.
Brandy and sugar."

A white-aproned vendor cried so, traditionally, his tray of transparent globules. He was at the head of the last lane into Oldham town. Eli asked of him, was there a theatre? "Oh, aye. Sideshows and circus, too, on the common by the theatre," the toffee-man said. They hurried on.

The near lanes and the new streets of the newly-growing town were filled with shows and show-placards, gaudily-painted: the first portraying the capture of a "POLAR BEAR" which must have been about eighteen feet high; it pawed and glared red defiance at brave sailors (oddly enough straw hatted at the Pole) who attacked it valiantly, heads at knee-level, their only weapons broad-bladed oars. Saffron-yellow lions impossibly stretched claws at barred tigers - all snarling, gaping of jaw but benign of eye. Snakes peered through improbable trees at bucket-headed elephants and monkeys and parrots of all colours and continents mingled in jungle harmony and peace, none timorously, all seemingly asmile. More placards advertised the side shows: a "Monkey on a Tight-rope", a "Pig-faced Lady", "A Horse that Spells and Sums", "The Living Skeleton", appropriately juxtaposed with a Fat Lady and a picture to suggest that no skeleton inhabited the flaps and folds of flesh. A Fire-eater belched flames at startled peasants. Tinier booths, dirty, equivocal, but morbidly attractive, fascinating concealed a "White Indian" (an Esquimau), a "Black Indian" (from Madagascar), a giant, a dwarf, the biggest child in the kingdom, a "Mare with Seven Feet"... and all had their mouthpiece, a "shouter", flamboyantly gesticulating as if to force the fair-goers to dubious entertainment.

It all seemed to excite Tom beyond measure; to Eli, critically observant but as always unspeaking, a disturbing excitement. He would have expected the shrewd, scathing-tongued Tom to have placed these garish cheats at peasant level. But the lively spectacle; the flaring naphthas and colzas, urging their oily and coal-tar odours into the evening air; the shouts and cries and "holas"; the flapping colourful placards; and the glimpses of the show-folk seemed to prick Tom to a hitherto-unknown gaiety of manner and to bring to his face, ruddy already, a new glow that, flare-lit, made him red as the devil. Usually taciturn, he made endless crude and bawdy comment on the exhibits, bringing Eli to rare laughter at his lewd suggestions about the Fat Lady, tantalisingly glimpsed through cunningly arranged tent-flaps.

Tom hastened them through the fair and its tributary lanes, as if searching... thence to the nearer inns to peer into their doors, until he pulled Eli into one and loudly ordered rum. He drank his half-tumbler at a gulp as if it had been water, urging Eli to the same. Then he hastened out again, face yet redder, while Eli's pale eyes streamed from the sting of the raw liquor. Into the showground again, this time heading towards the circus; Tom had muttered, "Maybe inside!" and Eli, hearing, shrugged and followed Tom into the tent. Tom was paying, rare treat: "Accept it and bother noan about why;" thus Eli, silently to himself.

This was for Eli, totally untravelled, a new world, and the ammoniacal smell of caged animals, the sawdust-and-earth and wet-rope smell, was to remain with him always; when encountered again it reminded him with more than nostalgia, for it was in those moments, he always averred to himself, that he knew... The dancing and tumbling clowns had gone, the enfeebled lions returned to their cages, the jugglers gone spinning away, and the trapeze-artists were practice-swinging in the high dim roof of the tent when one, a girl, turned full-face on her trapeze. She was indistinct of features but her legs were clear, trim in white tights and blue-spangled doublet; and Tom started to his feet. "There she be!" he cried and Eli had to pull hard on Tom's arm to get him down into his seat again. "Sit down, Tom," he ordered, then "Who be?" Eli demanded as Tom subsided.

"The platter girl; the ribbon-girl," Tom answered, but dully, as he saw now it was not she.

"Daft talk," said Eli, uncommonly bold. "Yon girl up there is fair; yellow as a buttercup." Then deliberately he added, "Martha is dark as a raven."

"Aye, I know." Tom's tone was flat, then it sharpened: "How dost know? Martha?"

"I've told thee, I deal with them now and again. I've asked."

"Did'st think her to be here, down i' Oldham?"

"It were likely, that's all."

"Chance yet, then?" but Eli merely shrugged in reply.

He protested vigorously, though, when Tom suggested they go and for once got his own way. Tom was different somehow, his mind not on domineering and intimidating, and he kept his seat, though wriggling and fidgetting in it until that last, ill-blown trumpet call ended the circus and they could go. It was raw-cold with a late-March frost and the showground and lanes were emptying fast, but Tom insisted on another walk round. Eli, having "set up" Tom once that night, complied. Round and round, up and down...until it was all just a daftness to anybody reasonable. At length they stood outside the circus again. "Let's go round the inns again, Eli," Tom demanded, incredibly.

"Nay, by God, I do not!" Eli cried out, in rare anger. "Not to see any bare-arsed lass!"

And he immediately stood back a pace realising he had released fury, as Tom raised clenched fists to his temples, snarling like a challenged fighting-dog. "No, by God, you bloody wouldn't - you no-man. What's a lass to you?" and again, "A bloody no-man."

"What dost mean?" Eli was deathly still, deathly quiet; and Tom was for the instant startled by a quick memory of the still weasel, pale-eyed too. But that Eli should turn was that a cur-dog should turn; and Tom flung in again.

"Tha knows well what I mean. Tha's never stood to a lass. Never could. Do I have to tell thee that?"

Eli did not reply; his face normally wax-pallid in the naphtha flares was white, but Tom took him for cowed and said, "Bide there a minute till I come back." And he strode away but when he returned there was no sign of Eli; and although Tom waited until the last flare was down, he knew that Eli was gone.

Tom hung about a few minutes as if reluctant to begin the long homeward march, as if he could not swallow a lost hope, but at length he moved off. Grumbling audibly, he earned a few sidelong glances from passers-by but paid no heed to them, his mind engrossed, obsessed. As he drew clear of the town streets and cottages and the new mills, the remaining influence of the raw spirit he had drunk in more than one inn began to diminish, and he lengthened his stride, half-expecting to find Eli waiting somewhere; but this he did not and soon put Eli out of his mind. He made little of the few miles up into the moor and, empty-minded now, seemed soon to come to his own cottage at Spring Grove; and he paused a few moments there, pondering whether or not to enter. The cottage was in darkness and Tom's wife and three children would have been long to bed. But it was more than ever tonight uninviting and he turned away, not out of consideration for those sleeping there, but more out of distaste and dislike. He would not be missed, he knew, nor brought to account for absence - not that it would have troubled him for a moment if he had - for often he slept up to his father's inn since the mother had died.

All the world seemed asleep as Tom approached the inn, the squat sturdy building a deeper blackness in the dark night. No light showed. Bill would have been hours in his bed. Not that his eighty-odd years had deepened his need for sleep; he was as tall and powerful as his son Tom; slower, maybe; greyer, surely; but strong as the oak timbers of his house. No, he would be away because customers but rarely came up the dark moorside, into the lanes which all manner of villains and tramps and rogues used in their mysterious journeys across the Pennines. None came, then, so Bill merely closed the thick front door; Tom knew where the side-door key was if he chose to lock it.

Tom walked quietly, a practised lightfootedness from illegal forays on the moors, made his way to the big rain-butt at the rear corner of the house and there paused, listening. He did not know for what he listened or why, but he was uneasy, aware. He did not stoop to feel for the big key behind the butt but stood still and tense. His eyes were somewhat accustomed to the darkness but he could see nothing, discern no movement out there. Finally, still not satisfied, he walked stealthily towards a big old elderberry bush a few yards on, at the bottom of the bankside. With fists clenched he rounded it... nothing. He peered up the short bankside to the drystone wall, but thought better of climbing up there in the darkness. He shrugged off his unease, returned to the inn and found the key behind the water-butt; the door was unlocked, though and he returned the key to its hiding place, taking little care to be quiet about that. Oddly careless and unsuspicious for a countryman, and in that country, but it seemed as if all suspicion was in and about himself, and he was careless of all else.

He entered and thumped the door to. There was a metallic clatter of heavy bolts driven home, then in the side windows the flash of a struck tinder-box, the flicker of a candle; this within moments at an upper window, just for a few seconds, then the whole inn was in darkness again... and this Monday evening ended in stillness and perfect quietness.

Neither the wife at Spring Grove nor the father at the inn had knowledge of the night-bird Tom that night; his absence was noted by the wife, if at all, with a thankfulness and by the father not at all, he being still asleep when Tom departed again. Tom had risen early, sleeping but ill in spite of a rum-induced weariness. He walked about, breakfasting off slices of cold beef on bread and a jug of ale. He moved quietly so as to be gone in silence; for hours he had been all alone in the world, or so he felt it to be, and that was how he wanted it. He was careful, though, to protect the inn for once by locking it; carefully he hid the key, using some stealth to do so this time.

He made haste to a copse where game sometimes ran and took cover from view as he passed through the valley from one moorside to another. He had set traps there, hare-traps and an illegal man-trap, should any man try to take his hare-traps; but on the first morning nothing, and again nothing this morning of Tuesday. So he made his way the few miles into Uppermill, for he was to see the constable of Saddleworth there, to look over the papers to a summons for a poaching affray on the land in his charge.

He was quickly away from the barrack-like little building that served as police-office; and he strode away cursing. The constable did not have all ready for him... all that long march, and he

18

was sure the constable had enjoyed his annoyance. Tom hastened back to the grove he had visited before. This time a trap had sprung and a hare fought on a fine thread of agony like a fish on a line, a thread soon snapped by a hard edge of hand. Back, then, a way to Madge's.

Tom, almost invariably dourly taciturn, was in a very different mood as he marched the curve of the lower hillside. Slow to change, he could not quite come to terms with the careful locking and bolting of his father's inn. After all, their doors had been left unlocked, day and night, these many years. Tom was, though he could not "place" it, suspicious of his own suspicion. "What's the bloody matter wi' me? Am I getting afeared?" and he spoke out loud, as he so often did when alone. That bloody constable too. Tom was sure he had heard laughter behind his back when he left the office - low and mocking, he seemed to hear it now. And awhiles back, when he had taken the hare, his hand had been bloodied a little and as he walked away he had faltered a stride or so as if dazed, mind swaying. The goading at his middle, frustrated a day, tensed him like one of his own man-trap springs; that and an angry excitement from his wasted morning spring-loaded his powerful body, pressed into his face a flush of blood to ruddy him up more than usual, so that that afternoon's bedding of Madge was a tempestuous assault.

Within minutes he was striding away, a magnificent athlete, making pace as if the violently physical encounter in the early afternoon had never happened.

He made quick way now to the moorland-estate manager's office. This was in the owner's grounds, where Tom knew he was not over-welcome. The massive crested gateposts and the tall "ironscroll" gates wakened in countryman Tom an ancient, deeply-residual, well-overlain feudal sense of subjection; just a flicker but irritating to an overlying sense of freedom born of years in the wide moors. As he walked the trim, wide, gravel paths to the office behind the handsome mansion of his master the flicker prickled the more, since Tom regarded the master here, and father before him, as a "Johnnie-come-lately", rich from the cotton manufactory during the Napoleonic Wars not long gone - and no moorsman, either of them.

He hastened to be round the building and to the office, and apprehension showed a little as he tried to walk as softly as possible in his heavy boots on the gravel. He did well to move with some circumspection for he got an angry, uproarious reception in the office. The estate manager was a burly figure in rough twills, beautifully booted, stalker hat at the back of his head, his dress carefully superior to the country dress of gamekeepers. His big, muttonchop-whiskered face was suddenly red with anger as Tom gave him a fairly offhand, "Afternoon."

"And bloody nigh eventide!" roared the manager. "Where have you been?" and when Tom looked a little mazed at this, "Where were you this morn when you should have been here?" Tom was so clearly surprised and shocked into dawning recollection that he was surely telling the truth when he said he had forgotten. "Aye, and I know what makes thee forget," was the rejoinder, speech broadening in anger.

"What dost mean by that?" but it was a question not demanding an answer, nor getting one.

"Wasn't tha to come here after the reading of the Pontefract charge to thee?"

"Aye. I remember now."

"Aye. I remember now," the other crudely mimicked, then, "I was in the village too and knew you had gone from the constable's station."

Tom kept his mouth shut and the other went on, "When I came out o' Brotherton's I finds this on my gig seat." He held up a folded note. "It's about thee."

"What about me? Who by?" Tom demanded.

"There's no name to it."

"And would'st take notice o' a no-man's letter?"

"Tha knows bloody well I wouldn't!" but there was a bluster in the manner of the saying of it that gave no conviction, and the manager got up to throw the letter into the fire.

"But what did it say, Mr Brierley?" Tom insisted.

"Naught but what I've heard afore."

"And that be?"

"Thee poaching. And, what's more, last year stealing game eggs for rearing. The new law has that as stealing, as you should know."

"I know the law - but I know naught o' taking eggs."

"I've thy word for it - but the grouse will be laying again soon and I'll be by thy side till the eggs hatch this year."

"Aught else?"

"Aye; Mr Ramsden wants thee. He's waited, too."

Without a word, Tom turned and walked out. He went across the cobbles to the rear entrance, where it seemed he was expected and he was shown in at once to the servant's hall. Here the master came to him to talk, much to Tom's discomfiture for he was well aware there would be sharp ears at any vantage point there might be around the hall. Tom returned a polite enough, "Good day, Mr Ramsden," to the master's curt greeting.

"Straight to the point, then," said Mr Ramsden. "I've had tittle-tattle again today from your manager, about your poaching, and I'll say no more than the grouse were damn poor for numbers last year."

"They can be," Tom said. "We agreed that last year."

"Yes, they can be; but need they be?" Mr Ramsden jigged up and down on plump little feet, comfortable paunch thrust forward importantly, face superciliously smiling. "But that I'll leave to Mr Brierley to settle with you this year. That's his country. But what's this I hear of you asking a rent of the gypsies - you call them the 'burnplatters' - up there on the moor out to Wessenden?"

"Seemed to me, sir," Tom was unusually deferential, "they might as well pay for having lived on the land - and off it."

"Oh, yes? And I wonder how much would come into my pocket, and how much into yours? Now listen, Bradbury. I want them off my land bloody quick. Or you and I will have a reckoning. I've not forgotten last year yet. Off you go, then; but just mark my words well," and he turned and went, leaving the other standing.

Tom, in a white-faced speechless rage, strode from the house with no word for anyone... strode out into a steady rainfall. After a moment's hesitation he went across to the stables - at least there would be none there with flapping ears, he growled to himself - and borrowed a coachman's long cape. That around him he hastened away, to be quickly out of the grounds, as quickly as possible out of an insupportably humiliating quarter of an hour.

He had little notion of where he was going, except that it must not be to his home, nor to his father's. He wanted to come face to face with none, just yet.

With no conscious thought in mind he found himself making for the high Wessenden moor. But now the rain was slanting down in steely whipping lines and he submitted at last, as he felt wetness on the bare skin of his shoulders.

He sought shelter in a deserted barn, seating himself on the steps of the loft-ladder, from which he could watch for the abating of the rain. But he waited long - the rain had the wildness of storm in August, but the steadiness of March rain - and as he waited, chilled from his wet shoulders, he sank lower and lower into gloom... a gloom shot through from time to time with a rage that seemed to glow redly in his mind; a glow more and more frquent until it was all one steady glow, and he sprang to his feet, shouting. Immediately he stopped as if surprised, as if the shouting had been from another. But he remembered what he had shouted, and he shouted it again: "They're all on my bloody back; all my bloody life: on my back; all of 'em... but I'll bloody shift 'em."

But the last few words trailed away as Tom cocked his head a little to one side as if listening to them - his senses were directed within him. From nowhere, from nothing it seemed, a flood of anxiety and fear brought his awareness of all about him to a stop, as if he were for the moment deaf and blind. He could not, then, see the dark grey rectangle of the doorway that looked out on the steely rods of rain pounding the soaked grass and heather, or the black walls around him. And he sank back on the loft ladder step, clutching at the stave below his seat as if to seek a hold on reality. Before an inner vision, behind his eyes, pictures of vivid intensity presented themselves: the schoolmaster flogging him and the sickening warmth, obscene somehow, of the body of the master by whom he was pinned to the caning table; the bruiser who had dug him in the back in the town pub - and before a girl too - and ordered him out; the beating of his last professional ring fight. Humiliation stabbed him and turned the knife. Panic-stricken, he jumped to his feet and fled. The cold lashing rain helped him as if washing the panic away, but his mind was now sharply attuned to his past, reliving the sequences of those mental pictures; remembering first, in the minutest detail, in lifelike colours, his boyhood and his newly going to school.

Chapter 4

Mrs Bradbury, Tom's mother, rose early throughout the year, as if some daily moral duty required it of her and this misty September morning was about the house and working when the old clock in the taproom wheezily spoke six. She liked the house cleaned, and free of last night's stale tobacco smoke and the strong smell of ale-soaked sand, before she called to "them upstairs" - she rarely addressed them or thought of them by their names - to have them down to break their fast since six in the evening gone.

At about seven she called up the stairs, "Thomas", three times in crescendo until she got a sleepy response, then, "Waken thy eyes; answer me sharper." Hearing his sulky, "All right, then," she clumped away on clogged feet to set up a wide skillet of frying ham and eggs over a fire brilliant in the newly-cleaned, high, black-leaded firegrate; an unusually full skillet for a good sending off for boy Tom on his first day at school.

There was little of alacrity about young Tom's footfalls on the bare wooden treads, little of enthusiasm about his face slowly appearing round the lowest baluster of the stairs and his mother sharply said, "I'll smarten thy gait in a minute, lad. Get to that

Two pictures found in an antique dealer's. The discovery of an "In Memoriam" card with the verses by James Platt inscribed in the churchyard of St Chad's, Saddleworth, suggests that these pictures may be of William and Thomas Bradbury.

slopstone and wash thyself waken."

Porridge first, and a big helping betokened an extraordinary day, but by that deepened the scowl on the boy's handsome face. Still, he held his tongue until he had finished and left the table to be out of range of his mother, who sat at the table corner to help him to his food. Then he said, "Do I have to go?" and stepped smartly back a little further as his mother, mannish of face and grim, rose to her feet with evident intention: "Start that again and there's a strap in yon drawer for thee. Thou'st been told; thy father paid good money for thee to go."

Tom acknowledged the inevitable by turning to take down his jacket and new little peaked cap. He donned these slowly, reluctance in every move, but his mother stood like Fate waiting, his schoolbag — a game-bag cleverly fashioned by herself — held out, in itself a reminder of happier use. He took it without further protest, without a word. "I've put thy slate and pencil-box in; and thy butties and an apple," Mrs Bradbury said. "And here's thy school-penny; bear this in mind every Monday. Now call upstairs to thy father, thou'rt about to go." But they heard the soft footfall of the father, coming stocking-footed down the stairs to see the boy away.

Husband and wife stood in the front doorway to watch Tom go. He went without a backward glance — he had no friendly wave or smile to give — and unwillingness showed in every line of his rigidly-held back and broad shoulders and in his heavy, thumping footfalls. Mother stood hands on hips, elbows outthrust, unyielding; but the father smiled a little, understandingly.

****

Young Tom was home betimes. He strode in through the wide open doorway, through into the kitchen where his mother was, took off his schoolbag and slung it into a corner. "Pick that up and put it behind the door, hanging up proper," the mother demanded. "Then pull up thy buffet to the table." This he did with an aggravating slowness and his mother sat down, cornerwise to him. "Well!" she said. "What'st done, today?"

Tom compressed his lips and was moments in answering, then, "This afternoon," he blurted out, "bloody dancing!" to get a clout over the ear that nearly knocked him off his buffet.

"Tha'll use such language to me?" his mother rapped out. "Remember where yon strap is. Now, about this morn?"

Tom relaxed his manner, putting the indignity of the afternoon out of his mind. The morning he had, in fact, enjoyed, though he came only reluctantly to that. The dame who took them was a good and devoted teacher, genuinely loving of her small class of boys and girls. Plumply cottage-loaf in shape and aproned, face rosy-apple in snowy wimple and mob-cap, she was kindness personified, gentling this big lad, rising ten but newly to school and seeming awkward among these others, mostly younger.

She set the others to work and then had Tom sit beside her at her table, slate and pencil ready. Like a good teacher she gave him what he could do with letters and with numbers; gave him a carefully arranged success and praised him for it. When playtime came he was in no hurry for it and after a few minutes of standing about by himself he returned, quite ready to take up the little set exercises again, fascinated with the mastering of them.

Dinner time was a lonely sitting about on the nearby wall. And a disappointment to follow. The little afternoon story was all right, even the little session of singing (he had a boy's silvery voice) but the dancing!! Outraged, he marched the miles home.

The dancing apart, Tom came to an affection for his school as he grew to regard with affection and respect his teacher, Mrs West. He delighted in his simple mathematics and his writing, or rather he loved to master them. To see Mrs West practising these arts so smoothly filled him with admiration. For her part too, recognising his unusual regard, she would write copy on his slate, sometimes even on paper with quill and ink; or would do simple Euclidean exercises, Tom at her side working through them with her; all to give the boy pleasantness, as one might play music for another, to please. She had, too, an affection for this lad who seemed but poorly off for friends - a little too ready with his fists with the boys, although he was no bully, and awkward and quick to temper with the girls, snortingly impatient as a tethered young bull. Even the dancing came to be grudgingly accepted since he could show off his strength when girls sometimes, in the round dances, would come to clasp hands and be swung around.

The worst of the winter storms did not hold him back from attendance, not until the fifteen and twenty feet deeps of drift snow off the peaks forbade him passage. And the spring and summer were a delight - a stern delight, for Tom remained a dour boy. Then the long walk down the hillside and along the valley was through moors putting off their drab browns for green and purple again; and the green plover swooped in insect-quick curves, its wings at a distance - always at a distance - seeming black, white-tipped; "lapping" as if to applaud its own "peewit" call. The drab-gray sheep sought the high ground again, ambling across his path, gazing at him with dim curiosity as he hastened down the long road to the tiny school. And sometimes there was mist, fog even since the mill-stacks and cottage chimneys were issuing coal-smoke down there; but Tom was always to school, pleased when Mrs West would say that he was one of few "to make the journey that morn".

And he was coming up to fourteen, tall, broad-shouldered, iron-strong for a boy, a smudge of golden-red bristle at his upper lip, when his days at the dame school came to an end. Tom was unhappy, hard put to express his sadness that Mrs West must leave the school - and him; and all the more hurt for not being able to express it. Mrs West had become a little tired, a little aged in effort. She had now to go to nurse her mother's time out, and the old dame three villages away, so that the mother's home in mid-winter with the roads impassable was as in a foreign country. It was not disputed then what a daughter's duty was; she must go to her mother and the little school close down. It would have had little chance of life anyway; as the upstart cotton trade thrived there was a growing demand in the widening parish for a bigger, parish school.

Time and the future had seemed to stretch away there in the
24

endlessness of days to come at school with Mrs West. And half-realised, taken-for-granted days in the sun, and in the snow, and in the mist and the rain were now brought sharply into memory. For Tom to remember the summer was schooling enjoyed in spite of some dream-gazing out of the open windows at the distant green hills; walks to the river for crayon-drawing; games in the tiny "yard" at the rear and among the fully-leafed trees. Spring brought to mind strange excitements and promises of summer, brilliant sunshine, sudden black clouds and showers; then out of doors again to colour-draw the rainbow; marbles and whip-and-top and the fast-running bowl. Autumn and mysterious mists, stolen fruit, harvest home and church. Winter and more snow remembered than ever fell; the snowman, snowballing, slides they called "slippy-curries"; sitting round the bright fire in the old iron grate and, when Mrs West was out of the room, spitting on the almost red-hot grate boiler top and watching the fast-disappearing globules run about like demented little live things. One of the little memories that, but a sharp one.

So came last day to end all that, dimming a great deal the glorious prospect of holiday. The school door was finally closed and Mrs West assembled her small class of all sorts and sizes for a final dismissal, for each one a separate goodbye. To Tom she said, "Bend you down a mite, Thomas Bradbury." He did so and she kissed him at the brow. "Will you miss the school and me, Thomas?" she asked, as of a son.

"Aye!" said Tom brusquely. "It'll hurt me," and he turned at once to make what seemed his longest walk home.

****

The summer holidays were as long as a year, and as short as a day, soon gone.

Brilliant July sun; torrential August rains, vivid lightning, and thunder cannonading throughout the peaks as if laying an assault to the ambushed wayfarer, trapped, not knowing which way to turn in the waterfall of rain. Dabbling fingers in the crystal water of the high streams on the good days, the flagstones warm as oven-plates to lie upon; on the bad days, listening to streams from the high ridges babbling down with newly-born fury. Walking, marching, occasionally running miles across the silent, lonely, high peaks with father's old lurcher dog making false little dashes at startled bounding hares - not dashing far, mostly content to keep at heel with the tireless, longstriding youth.

Until at last the first day back arrived, unwelcome. Down the moorland road again; past the old house at Nook Steer, heading the village cluster of cottages; past the little school, an instant's regret soon absorbed by the slightly-apprehensive anticipation of what was to come. The new school was a gawky, ill-favoured barracks of a house; a misconception of a "better-off" residence, built to the order of a cotton spinner who like many was well-to-do from the wars, and quickly abandoned as money began to flow south. It had a forecourt, now flagged with yardsquare gritstone and showing not the solitary green of a leaf or a blade of grass.

There seemed to Tom to be a great many in the forecourt compared to the little group of his previous school, and those earlier companions were almost as strangers now mingling with the new ones. So Tom's invariable friendlessness seemed likely to continue. There was little time for staring at one another, however, as they were summoned together by a loud shouting call. On the steps of the house was a little man, flanked by two others, younger, a man Tom correctly opined to be the head-teacher (new expression).

"Line up here in front!" now shouted the little man; a cry at once taken up by the other two. There was some shuffling into place, hasty because of the unpleasant bullying tone of the orders. A register was called, and there was another hasty shuffling into two lines and much discussion on the steps. In Tom, apprehension of the unknown had given way to the known; and the known was received with a scowling dislike. Tom, a shrewd, and in a limited way a lettered boy, soon felt himself to have the measure of the little man. He would have been hard put to define his dislike and his mistrust, but he saw the head teacher as a "half-and-halfer", farmyard expression; the little portly body clothed in a formal blue cutaway with proper high stock, but fustian breeches down below, gaiters over thick stockings and heavy boots. His face was red, his hair brushed modishly forward and he strode about with long strides, the strides of a tall man, which he longed to be. He fixed almost at once on Tom whose sombre, brooding stare, with his tallness, made him an outstanding figure.

"Stop staring there, that boy," ordered the little man, pointing. "You've been with the sheep too long," he added rudely. Tom continued his staring, unmoved; the little man marked him down for another day and busied himself now in marching the files into the two separated classrooms.

Tom's class was fortunate in its arbitrary coming-together in the charge of Mr Cream, one of the two who had flanked the head-master on the steps. It was a poor sort of good fortune, gaining only by comparison with the misfortune they might have suffered by being in the class of the other, Mr Ramsbottom, the son of the head teacher and a bigger, grosser version of his father. Clean on this day but most days unshaven, unwashed and unbrushed, he too was portly and red, but of fair height and great fat weight, a bully, pig-eyed.

Mr Cream was by comparison skeletal, shouldered no wider than a bottle, spiritless as he was bodiless. Fawning on all, he was grotesque before the older Ramsbottom, curving over when addressed by him and showing a fixed, skull's smile, eagerly agreeing with anything and everything. His teaching was an anxious pleading to do as he asked and as he said. No chance here of imaginative games in the afternoon and walks beside the river. Instead endless catechism; and dreary old learn-by-rote hymns and long-winded canonical prose from dim little cheaply-acquired books. Reading in turn, writing pious "copy" on to slates and tedious pointless sums very slowly filled the mornings.

Autumn's yellow-gold and crimson and the sparse fruits and harvests of the chill woods and fields were gone almost un-remarked, to make way for a drear winter of leaden-footed days; even Christmas washed almost to nothing in a sleety rain. Spring came, pale with too much rain but promising... games, and play again in the flagged courtyard and the ages-long winter school was through; for Tom only pointed up by frequent skirmishes with the Ramsbottoms, mindlessly picking on him, determined as they said to "keep him down", "that uppish Bradbury", but gaining little.

Spring in the tiny school play-yard this year seemed to bring a new awareness in the "year-on" older children; different from the infant sharing of pastimes, or of butties and apples while seated on the spring-sun-warmed low wall. Now there were vigorous games of close contact, boys and girls whirling together, the boys excited, the girls screaming excessively. One strapping lass, Maggie Sands, her pinafore-bib very well outcurved, made often to bump Tom Bradbury; but this she did once too often and Tom, quickly impatient of any hindrance of his running about, bumped back, full-shoulder. Maggie crashed sprawling to the ground, feet in the air, skirts high, but what caught Tom's fascinated gaze was the sight of Maggie's stocking-tops, full of holes - and laughter bubbled out of him. Maggie, furious, red-faced, scrambled to her feet and hastened away, flouncing and tossing her head like an angry mare.

It was an afternoon playtime, so that lessons afterwards began with dull reading, from an inevitably dull book, by Mr Cream. It gave Tom a fatal few minutes when he was not under scrutiny. The teacher's eyes well down to his reading, Tom had glanced back often at Maggie, two desks behind; she had grinned once, and at no time did she look to discourage the backward glances. Indeed, at last she gave Tom as frank a stare as his own and he stole quietly from his place to sit beside her. All the class saw the move but the teacher did not - Tom sat still to be sure of that - and then he slowly put his hand down and lifted Maggie's skirts... just to her knees so that he could see those fascinating stocking-holes again, but Maggie did not know that and she screamed, high and loud. Startled out of his seat and into stride, Mr Cream was instantly at her side, demanding an explanation. And Maggie, mistaken and quick to her own defence, cried, "He come beside me - I never asked him - and put his hand up my skirt!"

There were gasps of shock all around and juvenile hands raised as piously as any adult's, so that Mr Cream, immediately shunning responsibility, ordered a boy to bring Mr. Ramsbottom at once - and hurry! The head teacher rushed in almost within seconds looking pleased, delighted even, calling "Where is he? Where is Bradbury?"

Tom stood up, stepped into the aisle between desks and when questioned, replied, "I just wanted to look at her knees." Boy though he was, he realised how paltry an excuse that seemed, and when Maggie, anxious to keep herself in the right, averred again that Tom had put his hand up her skirt, he made no more denial.

"Come with me, Bradbury," Mr Ramsbottom ordered and led the way out to the "hall". There he ordered again, "Stand by that table," and he opened a cupboard and took from it a flexible cane, which he swished viciously in the air a couple of times. "Bend over that table," he commanded and Tom, standing fists clenched, said he would not. Instantly Mr Ramsbottom went to the main door, locked it and pocketed the key. He then walked to the second classroom

An early photograph of Bill's o' Jack's inn. The name Moorcock can just be seen over the door.

and called out his son, who came out in very spritely manner when he saw who was standing by the table.

"Take hold of this boy with me, Fred," the head teacher snarled. "Won't take his medicine," and between them they turned the struggling boy round and forced him over the table. But when the older Ramsbottom let go to take up the cane, Tom almost succeeded in fighting free. The two men together again forced him face down on to the table, and this time the younger Ramsbottom lay on top of Tom, using all his great weight and holding his prisoner's arms outstretched on the table. Thus obscenely pinned Tom fought and kicked; and when he felt the older one fumbling to lower his breeches to the cane he screamed like a ginned hare, and as helplessly. His screams were stopped in his throat with the searing shock of the cruelly wielded cane cutting across his bare buttocks. Outrageous pain silenced him, as his teeth clenched and his tongue seemed to choke him; he made no further outcry, though Ramsbottom thrashed him until his arm ached.

Tom bore himself well when he re-entered the classroom, showing no pain even when he casually sat down, it seemed on red-hot bars. But that evening, when the long painful walk home took him before his mother, his fatigue was evident, though the tearmarks were long gone. His father was in the kitchen too, and he looked up when Tom's mother said, "And what's the matter with thee?" Tom gruffly explained, omitting nothing, not even the account of his handling of Maggie. At this his mother, growing grimmer by the moment, was about to add her clouting to the boy's punishment when the father, as but very rarely, intervened. He did so with an authority the more marked for its rarity of utterance.

"Go upstairs," he commanded Tom and followed the boy up.

"Let's see if th'art marked," he requested quietly.

Tom turned, dropped his breeches and raised his shirt. "Bloody hell!" the father whispered. "Right. Do thyself up." He then went downstairs.

There was an angry altercation, then his father's voice was raised, authoritatively again: "Do as I tell thee, wife!" Within a few moments the mother entered Tom's room. Tom was staring out of the window and did not turn as she said, "Here: I'll put it on your chair. Just rub it in." And she put down a jar of salve, then, without a word, withdrew.

There never was another word about it, but the next morning Tom saw his father in the school; saw him through an inner window, but no more; they did not meet. All that day as on all remaining days, the head teacher Ramsbottom walked past Tom as if not there, clearly avoided contact, never spoke to him again - not even on the last day. That was not long in coming: Tom's father had said after his visit to school, "I'll have thee out o' yon by Easter. We'll quit proper. I've paid thee up proper."

So Tom worked his way quietly through to Easter, the Ramsbottoms obviously giving him a wide berth lest trouble befall them. And on the last day, freedom and Good Friday together welcoming him, Tom passed the Ramsbottoms on the steps, sparing them a long cool glance as if to bear them in mind; out into the road then, walking away from his schooldays.

Chapter 5

Easter gone, and many of the April days had been faithfully April. Pools filled the potholes of the rough country roads and they gleamed almost white from a pale sun; timid as a maiden this sun and, as shyly, disappearing frequently. Nevertheless, Spring charged the air full and young Tom Bradbury took joy from the morning and gave colour to it. He was mannish tall now, broad-shouldered; his redness very evident in the morning sun, arrogance in his swinging stride. He looked, and was, a fighter. He personified freedom in a free, fresh, green-hilly world. That he should be going for his first morning to the mill was so incongruous as to be incredible. And yet that is where he was bound – to the mill along the village valley and a little up the hillside. Reuben Platt had persuaded him to it.

Tom ended his schooldays with one friend only – Reuben. Not of an age these two; and there seemed nothing matching in their friendship, nothing to account for it, unless it was the attraction of opposites. Tom was frank and open, rarely and boundlessly generous, crudely so; but Reuben made him laugh, or at least grimly chuckle, at his petty, village-boy villainies and impudent wenching. Reuben was devious and false as St Mary's cracked bell – but he made Tom laugh. And he filled Tom's head with dizzying tales of Saturday night in the fascinating narrow streets of the new town, down the moors a few miles, tales only at second hand yet, tales at the village-inn door, ale-blown tales but tinglingly exciting to boys in the first thrust of Spring.

So there was money at the mill and money bought a way into town. The mill was of gray stone, solidly square and unlovely, forbidding. It was prison-like and a prison to its workers, for their waking hours were inescapably here; manacled by their poverty and by dread of the poorhouse, their only freedom was being released to bed at home, there to sleep against another day. The machines were their jailors.

Tom Bradbury had an aptitude for figures and surprisingly neat handwriting; these and the good offices of an underforeman, a customer of the Moorcock Inn, had secured for him a place as labeller, bill-writer, clerk, warehouseman and storekeeper; appren-tice-like in all these to an older clerk-man, a little privileged, and Tom too, for doing work the owner-spinner could not do. It was a good peg or two above the work of the machine-tenders, the machine-minders, the labouring poor and the pauper children and idiots of the countryside. Still Tom's mother, born of country folk only driven from their land by the Enclosures, was bitterly opposed to the "shame" of it. But the father, again on a rare intervention, had said that Tom might go, all his argument summing up when he said pawkily, "He'll stop of his own accord, tha'll see, wife – when he's had his belly full!"

Tom's mother was a farmer's daughter, knowledgeable of the lore of the countryside and of the farmhouse. But so, too, was Bill Bradbury of a farming family and he was of those farmers with a love of animals; particularly did he understand the handling and

gentling of young animals – when with a stallion coming newly to
working or to riding to use the curb, when the loose rein, when
the spur, and when the pat on the neck and the soft word. He
knew too that what drives a young stallion drives a young man
and Tom, rising sixteen, was early becoming one, a mannish boy.
So that the wife, her bitter tongue as wounding as her strap had
once been physically hurtful, would have created a sullen and
resentful young animal. But she was often banished to her stove
and the sink while Bill dealt more understandingly with Tom, as
he would with a full-blooded young "entire" stallion – one often
enough dangerous with rebellion of spirit when the mother had her
way.

The clash when first Tom prinked himself out for a Saturday night
was inevitable. Tom, with money saved from his mill wages, came
down into the kitchen in the early evening in country-boy finery:
whipcord breeches, velveteen jacket, fine stockings and beautiful
boots, but about his neck a smoothly-bound red silk neckerchief
tied off into a neat tiny bow. It was as a battle signal to his
mother and Tom defiantly wore it so. "And where art tha bound
dressed like that?" was the opening shot.

Tom delivered a reply that he knew he would have to give and
one which he knew by heart: "I'm going to the town, with Reuben,"
he flatly said.

"And looking like a fairground wrestler with that round your neck?"

Tom's answer was time-worn: "They all wear 'em!" and his
mother's response equally time-worn: "And who may 'they' be?
Lads as daft as yourself?"

Their voices had soon become raised and the father came in from
the bar. "I've customers in here," he warned. "Now, what's up?"

"This lad says he is going to the town – and look at that round
his neck!"

The words to forbid Tom to go sprang into Bill Bradbury's mind
and then he said, softly and to himself, as if to convince himself,
"Tha shouldst not stop a five-year colt from running."

Tom felt a flicker of pleasure at the expression so naturally used..
"five-year colt"... that meant "thoroughbred", and he said,
politely and to his father, "I'll do naught daft."

"Daft or not, tha dost not go away from here wearing that if thy
mother says not."

"What, then?"

"Take one o' my white stocks from my drawer upstairs and change."

Tom did so instantly; he had been quick-witted enough to pick up
that "not go away from here" and the corner-of-the-mouth smile
that went with it. Unusually, Bill Bradbury gave over the bar to
his wife for a minute or so and accompanied Tom from the house;
along the road that skirted the inn, past the barn-like stone
outhouse that served for a rough dancing and jigging room – and
even rougher drinking – and for the first time, and very gruffly,
"had a talk" to Tom. "Tha'st been enough in thy grandfather's
farmyard and shippons to know what coupling is?"

"Aye," answered Tom, equally gruffly. "I know; you needn't say."

"Right, then. So tha knows what comes o' coupling." Tom nodded and his father went on, "What tha likely dost not know is this: wi' animals it's all fairly clean-like. But wi' town women - aye, and some country light-women too, I reckon - it can be dirty; diseases that naught can be done for and a man soon finished." He paused, worried by the decisions he was having to make, then, "I should stop thee, but tha'd go anyway, and I'd sooner know where thou art. And someday, like wi' the mill, tha'll be o'er and done wi' it." He stopped then at the great square-pillared stone gateway to let Tom go on. Giving him a pat on the shoulder he said, "Tha'll contest it, 'bout doubt. But that stock looks better," and he smiled as he caught a glimpse of the red handkerchief in Tom's capacious side-pocket. "He'll learn," he said to himself as he turned back.

Tom met Reuben at the village end, so arranged by Reuben and a way out from prying eyes. It was autumnal dusk and exciting just for that, and the two made fast strides down the gently-sloping miles of the moorend road. A mile or so out of town they began to see a soft golden glow in the sky, now dark. They were passing rows of derelict cottages, mostly weaver-threestoreyed but roofless now, deserted, their occupants all - children too - forced by near-famine into the rapacious new mills that had destroyed their cottage life. To the two hurrying past, though, the dead hamlets through which they strode emphasised and made even more dramatic and enticing the promise of new ways of life, ill-comprehended yet but attractive, fascinating, to village boys.

Reuben, who had spent an excited week preparing for this thrilling excursion, seemed to know his way quite well; they had reached and passed the bottom of the moor and were now, still apace, on a slight rise. They passed a smithy, doors wide, fire aglow; smith in leather apron stooping, a horse's hoof between his knees. The boys hurried on; they wanted no reminders of country life, though the road they now walked was only a wide lane with an inn or two, a nondescript building like a warehouse, open-fronted butcher-shop, greengrocer's trestled front high stacked to sell until midnight, all cheerfully aglow with colza-flares, beckoning. And at the brow of the rise the parish church, its east end a faint dull pink in the light of the flares but mostly a dark, barely-distinguishable mass against the night sky, aloof as a stranger in this alien world, neglected where it had once commanded. It seemed to be a landmark for Reuben, for he said, "It's off here, last before the church, to the right."

They were to find the Trumpet Inn and they turned into a night-maze of mean streets, unpaved, unlit but for an occasional glimmer of a candle light from one of the long rows of back-to-back cottages mushroom-sprung about the new mills. Tinkling and scraping music at last led them to the inn door. A moment's hesitancy, then Tom led the way in. The landlord, stooping over the tapping of a barrel in the bar facing, looked up, and without word or change of expression jerked his head upwards. The boys went upstairs, narrowly enclosed on the far wall. They entered a long room and were at once wide-eyed and a little breathless, but they were promptly welcomed by a fat, smiling girl who requested money for tickets which they might exchange for beer.

There were about two hundred men and women in the room, which was cheerful in the glow of many candles and pleasant in that the walls were all painted with gaudy pictures: sea scenes; scenes from melodramatic plays; country scenes; coy animal pictures interspersed in total incongruity with diaphanously-clad Greek nymphs having remarkably bovine, village-maiden faces. Even the ceiling was painted with gauze-trailing cherubim, in would-be Italian manner and in the "grand house" style. At the far end of the room a shallow wooden platform was raised and a farmyard play was being enacted. The pictures on the wall were unexceptionable, given a visit from the parish constable or the churchwardens; but the play was something else.

Two very loosely-attired young women, quite prettily rouged and two beefy, leering young men, ale-ruddy, were playing the farmyard game; a third man, besmocked, country-style gaitered, unnecessarily flourished a coaching whip to urge on the two men to imitate the couplings of farmyard birds and animals - with the crudest dialogue from the "farmer" and the lewdest .actions and gestures by the "animals". It was all received uproariously by the half-drunk audience, by Reuben, already a pint of ale "down", rapturously; head thrown back laughing, he kept slapping his breeched thighs with whip-like cracks. Tom was amused in a somewhat different way. He laughed many times; but he gave the source of his amusement when he said, "Yon two chaps have never been in a farmyard."

It was all as gimcrack as any fairground catchpenny, totally false and empty, and Tom, a young realist, had soon had enough and hauled away the protesting Reuben, still half-hysterical with guffawing laughter. But the "play" was ended anyway and a scraping fiddle and toneless pianoforte, now beginning to play, hastened them down the narrow stairway and out into the dark, pounded-earth streets.

They sought the rougher taverns, Tom confident in his own young strength that he could deal with any town roughs, and soon they found in the older, tumbledown stone cottages near to the church - some of them seemingly of its age - a tavern that rightly belonged there. Even Reuben, excited and pleasure-seeking, was a little timorous at its doors. It had somehow the ancient evil face of a gargoyle but Tom, spurred by a different excitement, that of danger, insisted on entering.

The landlord at the rough, bare-wood serving counter was as foul of face as his tavern. Fat with his own ale, features almost lost in a pudding face, low forehead nearly hidden behind an oiled "cowlick quiff", his waistcoat not meeting but held together by a cable-like brassy watch chain, he was as sour as he was ugly. His greeting was a snarl: "There's little room here for country lads. Ha' ye any brass?"

Tom replied calmly, "Enough for you. We can pay our corner."

Grudgingly served, Tom and Reuben carried their own pots to a corner table. They had barely taken a pull when they were joined by two girls little older than they but womanish, grown, lacking any youthfulness; in town finery, fine cottons and feathers and fashionable buttoned boots; hair amass, piled high and topped by jaunty hats. One said impudently, "Two such bonny lads will not want to sit lonely." Tom, without a word, with his foot pushed into place two stools for them and the pert one, seated, said, "Very warm welcome! Next thing, you'll ask us would we like a drink to be friendly-like." She answered this herself: "We'd like a couple o' penn'orths o' gin."

Tom handed over the money to Reuben, who spluttered away on his errand. This was repeated two or three times while the talkative one, giving her name as Florrie, teased Tom with silly talk about "bringing the cows in" and "feeding the hens", to all of which Tom made cool, unperturbed rejoinders.

Soon the gin began to talk and Florrie, bold now from a large glass, was provoked by Tom's calmness and began a more serious teasing, opening out her pelisse to show magnificent curves stretching a half-buttoned blouse. Seeing Tom's lips tighten, and his gaze fix on the deeply shadowed cleft between her breasts, she turned on her stool, her back now to the others and to the others in the room, unbuttoned her blouse, then as quickly covered and buttoned again. "Now, did that stir thee?" she mocked.

Tom, a little lamely, began, "You are not like any girls I've seen before. You wear nice clothes."

"Nice clothes!" mimicked Florrie. "Quite the little squire. You shall see more for that," and she lifted her long skirts high to show fine red cotton "split-drawers". The two were now totally centred on themselves, tensed and poised. She reached to take his proffered hand to draw him to her, when Tom received a violent blow in the back, almost to knock him from his stool; and the girl swayed back, her face masked with fear, eyes horrified, upstaring.

Tom started to his feet, swinging around. Three men, standing triangle-wise, faced him but he saw only one clearly. He was barrel-shaped, powerful, wide at the shoulder. He wore a little cap like a skullcap, but with a button atop and a peak flat down over puffy eyes and a nose no more than a triangle of pounded gristle; the ears were smoothed of folds, meatlike pads with hearing holes. Tom, with experience of many fairs, knew this to be a professional "bruiser" and he waited for it. But some quirk in the other's dimmed mind saved him, for all the man said was, "This bain't no little lads' tavern. Get thee gone. Another time Is'll help thee on thy way."

Tom looked at the bruiser reflectively, fixedly, as if committing the face to memory, then he turned and left, Reuben scurrying after. "Thank Christ we're out o' there," breathed Reuben fervently, when they were out into the quiet of the dark streets again. "I were feared to death. Wert tha, Tom?"

"No," said Tom, and indeed he had not been. "I've never been feared of any man. But I'm not going home mauled up; not and face my mother. But I'll be back - when I'm the same size."

* * * * * * * * *

Tom and Reuben discovered the fair on their second visit to Saturday-evening town. To pass through it they were required to detour a little, quarter-circling northwards a half mile or so and

34

meeting the fair on the edge of the town, in it but not of it. It was permanent in some of its booths and stalls and in its "fit-up" theatre, all of these encircling and interspersing food stalls, old-clothes stalls, floor-level platforms of trumpery jewellery, hideously brassy watches and clocks gleaming so cheaply, brassily as would not delude any but the dim of sight or of wits. Pots and plates and cups and saucers, high-stacked, were clattered cheer-fully, pots and pans clanged together and raucous voices "pitched" these tawdry wares: "Not three shillings, ladies and gentlemen; not two shillings; here" - a stack of cups and saucers - "the lot, one shilling." Naphtha and colza flares lit the fair and the clouds and lent a little golden glow to the off-wandering ancient streets and cottages and the old church on the hill.

It was for Tom a dazzling, glowing little world through which he must pass to reach the darker, more dangerous excitements beyond in the town streets and taverns; and he always insisted on going this way, in spite of a protesting Reuben. So that the two country boys, one strikingly red-haired, the other black wavy-haired, both with polished-apple cheeks, came to be recognised by some of the sharp-eyed stall and booth holders and their "pitching men".

One Saturday evening a new cry had been added to the urgent clamour of the stalls and the booths and to the beseeching calls-to-buy of the food vendors: the gingersnap man, the appleseller, the oven-bottom-muffin man, the roastpotato woman, the dressers of tripe and the sellers of blood-puddings. It was a more commanding cry, a shout, hoarse and aggressive, a little off the main line of stalls. Tom, vividly alive to the now well-known fair, was at once curious to find the caller. He and Reuben made their way between two catchpenny booths and on to a little spare ground, encircled, almost as it were a green for the fair - and there was the new booth, high-platformed. Tom gripped Reuben by the arm. "It's a prize-fighting ring," he breathed excitedly. "Reuben! It's a prize-fighting ring!"

Reuben was less excited than Tom. "Well? What about it?" he said. The weekly wanderings in the fair were only to be endured while on the way to the taverns. He suspected here a new hindrance.

The front of the booth was as a stage proscenium, closed by ancient, once-purple curtains; and the proscenium "flats" were gaudily painted with stylised pictures of prize-fighters, tightly breeched, stocking-footed, stripped to the waist, fists up in the classical "guards", features handsome and unmarked... and in that very different from the three pugilists standing proudly, muscular arms folded as if aloof from the "barker" calling out these new "wares".

"Broughton's rules here, gentlemen." The caller made some pretension to the Corinthian "noble" style with which the "fancy" cared to surround the great encounters of the famous pugilists. He wore, too, a shabby travesty of the costume of the Corinthian "buck", probably a cast-off given to him: cutaway of fine blue cloth; high stock, once-white; hessians, and in a voice hoarse with shouting he continued, "A knockdown or a fall marks a round. Here's half a sovereign for the man who goes four rounds against the Kentucky Boy." He gestured towards the heaviest and tallest, a big negro, who raised his fists high in challenge. "The same rules, gentlemen, for the Thunderbolt, a man of middle size, and another half sovereign." The Thunderbolt raised his hands, too, in challenge and in salute, the while trying to follow an instruction, "Don't frighten 'em. Smile a bit; look a bit 'easy'." So smiling, a toothless grimace of startling ferocity put most out of mind of taking this one on. "Last," and this time the barker took the pugilist's hand, "one of your own Lancashire lads," and he raised the other's hand high. A youth this one, relatively unmarked; but of a bullet-headed inhuman blankness of expression that marked a difficult fighter. Not skilful but seemingly insensible to pain, and hard to beat. Him Tom eyed carefully; then said, "I want to see him fight, Reuben."

"Hey! It's half-a-crown to go in. Says so, on that board." Tom had anticipated this frequent ploy, and, open-handed as many times, said, "I'll pay." He was overheard by two or three of the regular stallholders who had come to hear and see this new attraction. They were boy helpers, sharp-eyed and endlessly curious, particularly of this tall, ruddy, well-dressed country boy who so often walked the fair with his blackhaired companion and who strangely commanded attention; aloof, and of an indefinable quality. They had tried to draw him in the past, and tried again now:

"Tha' canst get in for naught, if tha' challenge, Ginger," said one, grinning. But Tom merely shook his head, for the other promptly to say: "Art afeared, cocky-lad?"

Tom only looked a reply, but the other did not continue the jibe. "And three sovereigns for the beating of any one of these world-famous pugilists," the barker was calling; and Tom just made a feint-move with his shoulders that sent the jibing stall-lad back on his feet as if he had been actually struck, then took Reuben under the guard-rope, paid and entered the first booth.

Very rarely impressed by anything, even more rarely excited, Tom found here his first deep experience, and one most vivid and thrilling. The warm, male-animal smell; the sweet smell of the crushed grass on which the floorless booth rested; of damp, ancient rope and canvas; of pungent herb embrocations and oils; and an indefinable odour that might, faintly acrid, be recognised as that of the butcher shop, too.

Only one had challenged from the outside, appropriately a butcher of the town, well known and well backed by his supporters. He was massive; clearly, when stripped to the waist, of enormous strength; and he beamed amiably from a face as red as his own beef, his bushy whiskers lending only a spurious ferocity. He was a "heavy" and matched for the Negro fighter. His naivety, and that of his backers, was evidence that little pugilism of the professional kind was known and understood here. The ring was a roped square of boards making a foot-high platform. In the centre of this a yard-square had been marked out with chalk. This was the "scratch" to which each man must stand to begin the fight, and to which he must come after every round if he wished to continue. Half a minute was allowed to come up to the scratch.

"Flatfooted as a butcher" - the expression might have been created for the would-be pugilist. His broad back might have borne well sides of beef, but his feet were anything but nimble. He stripped
36

to good cord breeches and was impressive standing still; but moving he was merely a target for the graceful, lightfooted negro. Any one of the butcher's punches, ponderous and clearly signalled by the drawnback shoulder, would, if it had landed, have felled a bullock - and indeed it was claimed that he could do this. But he was punching at a shadow, and only occasionally would the negro allow a smacking blow to fall on his mufflered hands so as to make something of a show, although he was careful not to allow the butcher to get a grip for a wrestling throw. Those great arms looked capable of cracking a rib or two before the throw was made. And then the butcher himself hastened the end. Gasping, he demanded that the mufflers come off, though they could not have softened any punches since none landed. Shuffling, he tried to make a fight of it until the negro, a little startled by a grab of the other's great fists that came too near, in booth parlance "put the shutters up". Bareknuckled now, he began to hit straight and fast and the razorlike hardened knuckles cut up the butcher's face as if with one of his own knives. Almost sightless with blood from cut brows the butcher fought for survival, courageously trying to grab the elusive, truly black shadow. "If only," he panted, "I could get my bloody hands on thee!" The negro, not paid to take chances, heard that clearly and put his weight into a "finisher", a sledgehammer blow between the eyes that temporarily blinds a fighter. Two punches, a left and a right to the wind, ensured that the butcher would not clear the required half-minute and his backers could not get him to the scratch.

The "middle" match was farcical... town hooligans with a swindle they thought new: the challenger to go down unhurt, but in going down marking a round and so, by rapid dodging and going down, surviving the four rounds. In the third round he was not quick enough and got a short, punishing, good hiding, but he dodged smartly enough to make another fall. The booth-holder was bored with the wearisomely-familiar trick and disqualified the challenger for going down unstruck. "Match ended on a foul," he said, and took out a cudgel from his coat tails, while his pugilists gathered round to deal with any protests. There was no trouble; the payers in the booth, outraged by the swindle on themselves as well as on the owner, swarmed round the little gang of tricksters and threw them out.

Reuben, a little scared, and Tom, delighted but disappointed of the fighting, settled down after the fracas anticipating much from the young lightweight boxer much of their own age. So was the challenger, a bouncy brighteyed youth who looked a fighter, a strong, lively one. When the two new contestants faced each other at the chalked scratch, mufflered hands raised in correct guards, Tom leaned forward on his bench-form, as enrapt and as keenly observant as an expert buyer at the cattle-ring.

With little but village brawling in his ken, Tom analysed the styles, pugilist versus amateur bruiser, with an insight beyond his experience: the town boy's drawing back of the shoulder to put weight into a blow, but in so doing signalling intention almost as if he had shouted it and causing the other almost reflexly to lean away, or sometimes to beat his opponent to the punch. The booth boy punched straight from shoulders perfectly still, indicating nothing, weight put in by letting the body go

37

with the punch, the left foot always leading and balancing, so that his punches always met the other coming on. The booth boy, the "Lancashire lad" while in Lancashire, had the killer instinct of the first-class fighter; and Tom was as intrigued with the deadly mercilessness of his non-stop attack as with his beautifully poised and balanced style, his smooth gliding and manoeuvring, using his feet as neatly as a dancer. Tom realised that it was the cold instinct, regardless of generosity or sporting "let up", that invested style and expertness with the sure surge of conquest.

Twice down, the town boy made an all-or-nothing attack in the third round. By sheer fury of his whirling fists he crowded the booth boy into a corner and there fought him for it. Neither made attempt to grapple for a throw; the town boy specially dare not allow a moment's pause for what might come through to him in that moment, for he was conscious only of the snake-like glittering eyes, facing him unflinchingly and showing a ferocity waiting to be unleashed. Until at length strength began to fail as violent sustained effort, ill-applied, gained nothing; there was no chance at all. Shoulders sagging, fists dropping, he began to take his punishment; a blood-spattering, thudding onslaught by one who in a cold fury paid off the "raw 'un" for daring to hustle him into the limits of his ability. The town boy kept on fighting in the retreat across the ring, until there was nothing left and he collapsed finally as unconsciousness buckled his knees.

They were a very rough crowd that had seen their "townie" go down; they had cheered him on, yet they too at the end had roared for the "kill", bloodlust supreme. Yet again, volatile as any sporting crowd, when the feverish lust died down and the booth-owner had shouted that the town-boy challenger would get his half sovereign as a "good loser", they were generous in cheering this and in throwing in their coins, the clinking and clattering of which helped the boy's return to consciousness. Tom went down to the ringside to throw in his contribution too, but curiosity impelled him there as much as did sportsmanship; and he studied with narrowed speculative eyes the areas of injury and bruising, the swelling between the eyes, estimating the weakness of defence and the strength of the attack. He studied, too, the winner. With an angry red patch over the heart, the fighter was now stripping off his mufflers, back to the ring and oblivious of the other, who might not have existed as far as he was concerned; his flattened profile almost smoothly featureless and expressionless as a curved line; not merciless as much as not knowing mercy or human feeling - a fighting animal.

Tom pondered all this. He was totally enrapt, fascinated, and though he had not yet acknowledged it to himself, he was working it all out how to win; coldly, surely; no lust for blood or for injury; simply to win, to conquer. Outside the booth, Tom could not contain his enthusiasm. Within the hour, in the little canvas-enclosed world of fighting men, he had become fanatical, as in nothing ever before.

The playhouses and taverns were of little interest to Tom that Saturday night; the excitement and fascination of the tented world of fighting men were still vivid with him and the crude, bawdy plays were sour skimmed milk after the tingling raw spirit of the booth. He felt deeply involved and committed to engage, himself, in what he saw as the supreme manly sport. Its stylish athletic savagery appealed to both sides of him; he loved the thoroughbred male and loved, too, the courage that asks no quarter and has no limits.

With all that, he suffered in the days following the endless prickle of frustration. He knew only Reuben well enough to ask him to "put on the mufflers"; this in the barnlike squat stone building that stood before the inn, the so-called danceroom. In here Tom had rigged up a simple "ring", squared off by a single rope, and in it tried to slake somewhat his avid desire, not merely to fight - that had rarely interested him - but to exercise his already burgeoning knowledge of pugilism, to fight so as not merely to injure, but to show speed, elegant balanced movement and whiplash punches, to show mastery thus of the manly sport.

In this ring Tom had soon to be satisfied by, as he said to himself, "fighting nobody", moving lightning-footed and punching on the move, cleanly. Reuben had given him one or two reluctant encounters, each with fists in home-made mufflers, and Tom had been careful to keep his fingers slack, sometimes striking only with his fingertips, satisfied to score the touch, delighting in his speed in attack and in defence. Then, in an intricate feinting move, long thought-out, he bore in for the decisive punch, fist tightly clenched, wrist straight; and Reuben, too clumsily raw to ride a punch, one that he never saw begin, went down as straight as a plank and lay breathing stertorously.

Tom, contrite - he had only, in a moment of complete absorption, forgotten his gentlehandedness - rushed out and was back in a moment with water and brandy; to find Reuben already sitting up and refocussing his blurred eyesight, shaken and angry. "That's all o' me for that bloody game," Reuben growled. He was in no way averse to a fight in the "rough and tumbles" as the village boys called them, but this was something different. He felt as if he had been struck with a heavy hammer, expertly wielded, and nothing Tom could say could make him come into the ring again. So Tom "fought nobody" until it began to seem futile to him; and he was about to give up this strange unrequited love when Chance gave him his opening.

On the Monday of the following week he chanced to leave the factory at dinnerbreak-time, to go into the village. On his return, he found a small group of the younger factory-men excitedly laughing and cheering, all in a ring with something going on at their centre. He would normally have gone on past them; he rarely came into contact with them; but there was an odd attention-catching note about the clamour and he walked so as to pass them more nearly. It was a commonplace factory-yard event: the bullying tormenting, sometimes torturing, of some poor factory butt. This one was different, a boy yet but white of hair, strange until one saw that he was pink-eyed, albino. Under the raucous bullying note there was another more sinister, that of hatred of the "different", the "abnormal"... and the "plaguing", as they called it, was becoming charged with menace. The lad was strangely named Eliphalet, and the jibing had begun with a silly, joking teasing: "Elephant! Here's a bloody great elephant!

39

Elephant! Elephant!" There was a little inverted humour in the inappropriateness of the jibe; there was nothing elephantine about the slim-shouldered wraith, pointed of chin as an elf. Short, too; boyish and no likelihood of manliness. He just cowered under the jeering, now clearly menacing and ugly.

Tom might have walked on, unmindful of a common enough little factory-yard scene, but he had come close in curiosity to see the object of the excitement and one of the mob, a mite crazily excited, burst out of a ring to get a new position and cannoned into Tom's back. Seeing who it was, he swore furiously, "Get out o' the bloody way, Bradbury," evincing a dislike generally held for this aloof, different-style, young writer-clerk.

There was an instant of silence as Tom turned towards his loutish challenger, then as the two faced each other, clearly for some sort of settlement, the mob, sensing a greater excitement, abandon-ed their victim. In an age-old common movement they formed a ring, so that one or the other must back down or settle it with fists. If it had been a few days earlier Tom might have shrugged it off, neither the incident nor the challenger being of any account, but now he felt a new excitement of the skill and power in his fists and without a word took off his coat, as clear a gauntlet as any. Tall and powerful in his shoulders now, he was not yet full "made up". His opponent, older, in his early twenties, was set, solid and clearly massively strong. He too took off his jacket, grinning around confidently at his friends. The ring backed off to make room and made its support instantly clear as the yells began: "Come on, Cleggy! Give it to the bugger!", "Get stuck in!" and "Cleggy" came forward, arms out bear-hug fashion, to crush by sheer strength as he had often fought before. He was stopped dead by a flush hit in the mouth and he backed away, eyes watering from the tingling, jarring shock. But he did not move quickly enough, nor could he, for Tom followed up in balance, left foot leading, and he moved with predatory speed. He feinted a left hook low, then looped that left over the other's dropped guard, a flush hit in the eye, almost instantaneously followed with a right cross to the other eye. Momentarily blinded, Cleggy knew nothing of the tap to the chin that lifted his head back for a wicked punch to the throat, from which he dropped to the ground in self-defence, shocked and be-mazed. He was dragged to the side of the ring, where supporters "made a knee" for him and gave him a generous rest.

He came up to scratch glowering, grin quite gone and made slow and ponderous opening leads, but he was not allowed his own speed. Tom dictated that, moving in gracefully but powerfully like an animal going in for the kill. It was deadly; and the crowd was quiet now, tense, more than a little scared of this silent, murderous assault, for the slicing crosses and hammer-like straight punches had in minutes torn and pulped the other's face. Cleggy again went down for shelter.

He seemed to come up to scratch again under instruction, for he made no attempt to lead, but stooping a little, shielding his face and throat with his arms and peering through his fists, he bore in, clearly to attempt a grapple. His evident great strength made this a real danger; but Tom, eyes narrowed in concentration, changed his balance to feet astride, then, as a bullfighter before an enraged bull, pitted skill against strength. He reached forward and took the other's right wrist and acting with urgent speed tugged him forward, turned, put his right foot behind the other's right and arm about his neck - and threw. It was a good cross-buttocks throw, not overly skilful but efficient enough; and Cleggy went up into the air and came crashing down on his back, on to the "kidney-cobbles", with a bone-shaking thud that caused all around to gasp in sympathy and to make O's of their mouths. Cleggy made attempt to come up without a rest, but he was stooped with the wrenching of his back and Tom stood aside, hands unclenched down at his sides. The fight was over and Cleggy, bewildered, was led away, leaving Tom inwardly exultant. It had been a test.

Tom looked around for his coat. Eliphalet handed it to him and Tom glanced down at the boy looking up at him with pinkly adoring eyes and took the coat, giving Eli a half-smile in acknowledgement. He had quite forgotten about him.

One of the men workers awaited Tom at the mill door - Bryn Hughes, the underforeman, who had put him in the way of coming to this mill. "I saw the fight, lad. Maybe I should 'a stopped it. The gaffer'll want to know some aught of it; yon Clegg'll fettle poor today. But I were spellbound, Tom. Wheer did tha learn that? A real pugilist, the best I've seen in these parts and sin' I came up from the valleys."

"I got very taken with it, Bryn, at the booth in the town a while gone. I saw a lot and learned some of it, but little chance else of learning more here. Nowhere, is there?"

"No. not here. But there is in the town. I go most Sunday after-noons. There's a place there you should see, if tha wants enough. And, for that matter, some pugs I'd like to see thee. Tha's got something there, Tom, I tell thee - and I've seen good'uns."

"Where then, Bryn?"

"Dost know the Spotted Cow in the town... downhill this side a bit from the church, main road?"

"By sight. I've not been in."

"Nor needst tha. There's an archway farside, and a room over the arch. Go through the archway, there's some empty shops. Meet me there. That is, if tha'rt keen enough?"

"I'm that," said Tom briefly, but the other was satisfied.

"I'll see thee Sunday, then. Say two o'clock."

Chapter 6

The Spotted Cow had been a Lancashire-Yorkshire coaching inn, ended as such by the main Manchester routes. Tom walked into the old coaching yard and looked around in puzzlement. He was early and the yard was quite deserted; nothing stirred. But at length he noticed a glimmer of movement in one of the empty shops; there was a short row of these below a broken-down first floor gallery,

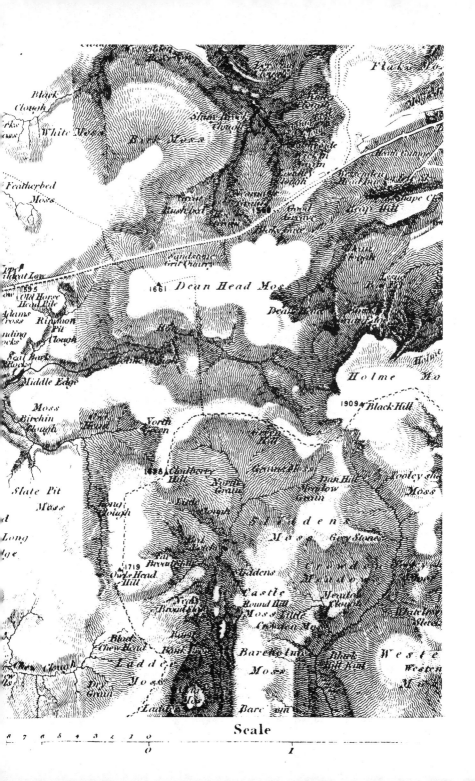

Scale

shops that had once served the coaching passengers and were now abandoned, long derelict. And again the glimmer of movement seeming to circle behind the bottle-glass panes. So Tom moved to press his face up close in curiosity. The blurred object suddenly resolved itself by also moving up to the glass. It became identifiable, though grossly distorted, as a broad white face, toothless it seemed, and evilly grinning. Tom turned away, startled, and retreated to the empty archway, where Bryn Jones soon joined him, to be told of the face in the shop window. Bryn laughed. "The Tinker. That's who you saw. We've come to see him. Follow me."

They pushed open the door, setting jangling an ancient dangling bell and Tom kept close to Bryn's side as he stared at the grotesque tableau of an enormously wide-shouldered man, squatting like a toad and having each fist in a bucket of water, one each side of him. The man's nose was so flattened as to seem mere nostrils; his cropped, bullet-round skull, bearing ears like short-stemmed mushrooms, settled upon a vast neck that spread broadly into his shoulders; and his open mouth was toothless, wide, again toadlike. "Good day to thee, Tinker," said Bryn cheerily. "Here's the lad I spoke of this morning." To Tom: "This is Jos Palmer, Tom, though he's been called the Tinker so long not everybody knows his real name."

"Be true, that," said Jos and his voice was a clear, gentle treble high as a boy's, so that Tom was startled a second time, almost into smiling. But Jos was eyeing him carefully so Tom stood impassive, relaxed and at ease; and the other noted the sloping wide shoulders, body wedge-shaped down to slim hips and long muscular legs, breeches and stockings well filled, and the boy's steady, confident gaze. "Right," said the comically treble voice. "Strip to the waist." Tom did so and Jos stood up, his hands dripping. Catching Tom's curiosity he explained, "Soaking 'em in brine; toughen the skin on my knuckles. Cheaper than alcohol. I've a bit of a battle tonight." They shook hands and Tom felt the hands like tough, wet leather. "Now," said Jos, "just pull me around a little, wrestling style, if tha knows it?"

Tom nodded and began... and began very soon to feel foolish, as he seemed to be trying to move a rock, changing from push to pull, twisting and turning his efforts, feinting his turns but always being countered by the subtly quick counterturns that seemed always to present him with a solid immovable mass. And he gave up at length, saying, "No use," a good deal crestfallen.

"You're a very strong boy," said Jos. "That's all I wanted to know. Don't worry tha couldn't shift me. Tha couldn't; not using thy feet." He pressed thumbs into Tom's biceps, then: "We want them as smooth and soft as silk - till tha uses them. Then tough as sail-canvas. All thy muscles. Put thy jacket on, over thy shoulders. We'll go up to the ring."

They crossed the yard to the archway, to enter by a wide stairway a room serving as a gymnasium, surprisingly large, spreading across the arch and over all the inn rooms, the entire top floor. A large ring of padded posts and ropes raised on a very solid-looking plank platform occupied the centre, surrounded by tiered bench seats. At the end spaces a clutter of training gear: rope rings from the ceiling, bar bells, a great canvas punching-sack, a leather-topped box-horse, and a table with a row of

44

padded mufflers. Tom breathed his delight. "Can I come here, Tinker?" he whispered.

"Dost like it, then? I built it all. I'm a carpenter by trade. Prize money paid for it - and a bit o'er." Jos grinned his terrible grin. "And let's see how tha shapes, if tha wants to come here regular-like. So get in the ring. We'll 'loose-knuckle' for a start. Bryn, take his corner. Two minutes at a time for a start. Time us careful."

They took the centre of the ring, Jos adjusted Tom's guard and they began. Jos looked now very much the prizefighter; he glared, feral, menacing, while Tom, red poll of hair lowered a little with the intucking of his chin as he had just been taught, poised, elegant but wary, returned with an intent stare the other's glare. Suddenly there was a pouncing flurry of movement, left hands striking like snakes, each right hand whiplashing to the head. Loose-knuckled as they were, Tom showed one or two red patches where Jos's knuckles, pickled to a rough, undressed leather, had hit "on the glance"... and his nose was red. He now backed away from a straight left, then neatly side-stepped his way out of a series of scything right hooks. Absorbed in this, he missed a change of stance and the Tinker - the "Jos" was lost in the prize-fighting pugilist - eyes gleaming, sprang in to gain the advantage from his right-handed attack. With unbelievable grace and lightness he turned his back and jammed hard against Tom's belly; he reached up a gnarled branch of an arm round his neck, then stooped to complete the "flying mare" throw but, back turned, failed to see a glint of triumph in Tom's eyes. Tom slapped his flat hand, fingers spread, into the small of the Tinker's back and pressed hard, and the Tinker now might as well have tried to pull Tom's elbow-locked arm through his body. Before he could release his hold he was hoisted off his feet by Tom's straightening up. Both now released holds and the Tinker dropped to his feet and turned, laughing heartily. "I had not gi'en thee credit wi' knowing that," he said in fluting treble, higher still for exertion - he had had to move sharply. "Another round, fast as tha likes," he ordered now.

This round ended after a whirling onslaught and counter-onslaught in which Tom was outmanoeuvred often into the outside of fast-turning circles, so that the sheer speed needed to resist a furious but open-handed attack caused a moment of total concentration on hitting and, as with Reuben a few days before, he closed his fist and struck. It hit the Tinker fortunately a little high on the chin and mouth, and it cracked home with a sound as of two pieces of wood slapped together. The Tinker growled a little; it had knocked his head well back and Tom was instantly apologetic, truly contrite. "I'm sorry, Mr Palmer," he cried. "I forgot myself."

His concern was so evident that the Tinker at once put on his terrifying grin. "Ne'er mind, lad. Oe'r-keenness, I reckon. Tha'll not be one to foul." His amiable words came comically treble through the ferocious grin. "But that'll do for now. I don't want to start tonight with a sore mouth. And now, laddie, whe'er did tha learn wrestling tricks?"

"My father," answered Tom briefly.

"Well, ask him to wrestle again. As often as maybe. Don't your father have the Moorcock up yon moor road, opposite the Pots and Pans?"

"Yes."

"Then bear this careful i' mind. Art wanting to start fettling here? Readied for fighting by me?"

"Am I good enough?"

"Tha wouldn't be asked if tha were not," Jos answered drily.

"Then aught you say. Aught at all."

"Canst come Tuesday night, Thursday night, Saturday noon?"

"I'll do that," said Tom. "Times I'll come down on the cotton waggons. That or on my feet, but for sure."

"The whiles, remember this: staying power matters most of all. I'll not say how good thou art, not yet; but the best must have staying power or mostly lose. So listen. Run up yon Pots and Pans hillsides... steepest you can; like fell-racing, say. And run down, too, fast as you can. Lighten your step. When it seems easy fill a sack wi' aught - turnips, stones. Lay it across your shoulders and run the hill face again. And if tha'st a bit o' spare ground or a spare room, an empty shed, take thy shoes off and fight around in it on thy own - fighting a ghost, like. Off tha goes, now. Be here, Tuesday." Jos ended by giving a thumbs up sign to Bryn, who knew to take from that that Jos thought the boy to be a good one, a very good one.

Tom was completely diligent, his mind devoted to the absorbing fascinating game, the man's game. He was scrupulously careful of his training on the steep, almost sheer moorsides up to the peaks, and although he stayed down in the town on the Saturday afternoons after training, this was to please Reuben, who saw little of him nowadays. But Tom was faithful to his training even then, taking his evening meal in the best pie-and oyster shop in the town and limiting his drinking to a couple of glasses of the best ale. He then sauntered round the inns, amused by the antics of the soon "overtaken" Reuben, who was as diligent about the other "man's game".

In the fourth week, after a sparkling display against a local young pugilist, both "mufflered" as to fists but fighting stylishly and with determination, Jos wanted a word. He took Tom to one side quietly. "Look'ee, Tom laddie. Miss Saturday this week and come down on Sunday, early noon. Tha'll see the place different than when tha first came on a Sunday. It were empty then, 'cause I'd a fight that night. Different I say tha'll find it; and I reckon I shall have a match for thee. No prize, mind thee, but worth thy while, that I'll be bound. Dost take it?" and he knew he need not have asked.

Different it was; more than a hundred people: a dozen or so of the regulars, crop-haired, flat-nosed, ears punched to smooth tabs but bright of eye, springy of step; then butchers and bakers and every trade and, it seemed, purse; but chiefest of all, the "bucks".

These were mostly lads in their twenties; sons, almost all, of wealthy millowners and woollen merchants, they made very close

46

copy of the "dandies" and "heavy toddlers", "bucks" and beaus" of the metropolis, the swell supporters and backers of the "fancy". Beautifully dressed they were, indeed London-dressed, in green or blue cutaway coats with gilt and silver buttons, tight buckskin breeches and glossy Hessians all overtopped by extravagantly-curved beaver hats. Faces were adorned with, mostly, somewhat scanty whiskers. There was a good deal of flourishing of snuff-boxes, and equally a good deal of surreptitious sneezing. A little prinking, more than a little posing; nevertheless, all were lovers of the "fancy", all, no matter how inexpertly, ready to have a go in the ring.

One of these Jos set to one side, then brought Tom to him. "Here he is, sirrah – young Tom Bradbury," and to Tom, "Squire Bromley's son, Harry. They are from Cheshire and I'd like a good report o' thee to go back to the squire. Now, Mr Harry would like a turn in the ring wi' thee. Art game?"

"Naught so sure."

"Strip off then, sirrah, and get mufflered. I'll tend to Tom, for the same."

In a corner, Jos muffled Tom's hands, and at the same time, in a high, sibilant whisper, primed Tom. "Tha' gives away height and weight, laddie," and Tom looked across corners at his opponent. Harry Bromley had a couple of inches or so over Tom's six feet and he was heavy, but magnificently muscled. Had he been other than wealthy, he too might have fought for prizes. As it was, he just loved to fight, to box. "Give no more than tha gets, Tom. Remember he's a gamesman, fighting for the love of it; but a good 'un could hurt such, badly."

"How if I'm at the losing end, Mr Palmer?" laughed Tom.

"That'll be accident, lad. He has a punch like the kick of a horse, but thee like the kick of a racehorse; and that can kill a man."

Jos's professional prediction turned out to be the correct one. Harry Bromley fought well, struck with his weight behind his fist, but most often struck air or a guarding glove. Once he had laid a flush hit to Tom's chin that caused Jos to look anxious, but Tom absorbed it in a way that satisfied his trainer and immediately went in to give as much as he had got. Moving with astonishing speed he manoeuvred Harry into a corner and then dropped him like a stone... just two blows, a left and right, both upswung a little for height, that lifted Harry on to his toes before he crashed to the boards.

There had been almost total silence as the fight went on, a silence of absorption in a new, fascinating style, absorption with the grace and strength and courage of it all, in contrast to the fierce cheering and shouting of the booth, the lustful cry for blood. The young pugilists-in-training were wide-eyed and pressing up to the ringside to see it and to learn, cheering generously, after the manner of their kind, at this end to the first round.

Tom boxed the second round, for his own instruction working his way through moves and attacks, as he had for hours practised fighting alone, fighting "the ghost", as Jos had asked. And Harry, bewildered and frustrated endlessly, at last felt the surge of fighting fury, summoned all the strength of his young giant body and flung himself into a tearaway assault that by sheer force would have carried against even a very good opponent. But he landed few telling blows and the other's calm, though wary, keen gaze dismayed him a little. Still, he achieved a speed of attack quite extraordinary in one so huge of frame, and Tom now had to give as good as he got; indeed, a thrashing was only minutes away and he came forward, menacing and deadly, yet calmly calculating not to batter the other's face. Instead he struck to the body half a dozen or so blows that must indeed have been like the kicks of a racehorse, and many on the benches winced and frowned as if they had been struck. Harry slowed as if his feet had suddenly been shackled, his eyes were dull with shock and pain and Tom, showing great consideration for a gallant fighter, with a right to the heart brought his opponent's head forward and then neatly clipped him on the jaw to put him down.

Harry did not come up to scratch again. Jos explained to Tom kneeling and resting in his corner that Harry's ribs were too sore, maybe one of them "gone". "Get washed and dressed, lad," he ordered. "But give your hand to these lads. Tha'll make a lot of friends today." And so it seemed as the young bucks crowded round to shake his hand, and the young pugilists cheered him again.

Tom went to his corner of the gymnasium to wash and to dress. When he had finished Jos was waiting to speak to him. "Here, lad," he said, and held out a beaver hat, crown down, "The swells have put this in for you."

Tom took the hat. It held a "floor" of sovereigns. For a moment he was hesitant and looked up at Jos, who promptly read his mind. "Take it as thy first prize money, Tom lad. It's given with a good heart; tak' it so. Like clapping and cheering, it shows they've taken to thee. And that's half a stone on your weight to have the crowd behind thee. So put these sovereigns in thy pocket."

Harry Bromley came across then, stooping a little and a little leaning to his left as if to ease the breathtaking ache of his sore ribs and torn rib muscles. He was smiling, albeit a shade ruefully, and powdered and pomatumed once more, ribbon in immaculate bow at the back of his wig, he made a good show of languid insouciance. As part of the code he gave no sign of the beating he had just had and his modish drawl held not a quaver to show the painful effort it was just to speak: "You know, young Tom Bradbury, I fancy I shall boast one of these days that I had 'em on with you." He turned to Jos Palmer. "Have we got another Jem Belcher here, Jos?"

"That would be a bold thing to say, sir," said the cautious Jos. "But they do say as Jem Belcher fights scientific and so does this lad." He frowned a little at Tom. "But dunnot take on so, if I says that. I've seen swollen heads get some rare thumpings." Tom smiled and nodded understanding.

"So, young Tom," Harry broke in, "would you fight for me, if I find you a match?"

Tom, a little out of his depth, turned questioningly to Jos, who promptly asked, "Had you somebody in mind, sir?"

"A protege of my father's," Harry said, and added drily, "One who has taken a couple of purses, and lost me a couple of wagers put up with the purses."

"But this lad has ne'er fought for a prize," Jos warned.

"And my father's boy has," agreed Harry, "and he is a good strong fighter - what you would call a tearaway style, Jos. But young Tom here has something different; something coming along new with Jem Belcher and one or two more. Anyway, I'll put up another purse and double my wagers, so that's what I think; said with sovereigns, you might say."

"Thank you," Tom said simply, then, "I shall have to speak to my mother and father. I'd not go against them."

Harry Bromley looked a little surprised; here was a fighter out of a different mould, he thought, of an odd distinction and manner, but somehow this gave him even more confidence that he was giving something more than money to the sport he loved. "Very well, Tom," he said. "If I send a letter here by tomorrow's mail coach to say the match is on, will you send a letter back to say if you are on?"

Tom, on an approving nod from Jos, agreed.

Chapter 7

Tom got his letter confirming the match; but more than that, he was to bring Jos for his corner, and if possible one of the sparring boys for a couple of warming-up sessions the evening beforehand. They were all to stay at the Crown coaching hotel in Manchester and journey down into Cheshire in good time on the Sunday morning. For hotel and all coaches Harry Bromley would pay.

Jos Palmer had little difficulty finding a partner - young Benny Oliver, by courtesy so-called. A "bye-blow" of the Ribbon Fair and a merry evening with the recruiting soldiers, he had only a slack mother who never gave him nay, even to going with fighting-men to the faraway city, all of a day's carting away. He was a merry lad, bubbling with glee as if the merriment of his making had stayed with him, and Tom was glad of his company. Only once had he been to the city, as a boy with a carter, customer at the inn. The fourteen miles to Manchester and the return had taken all of the day, and he had seen little but the inside of a warehouse. Benny, full of delight, had not a scrap of the diffidence that restrained the more reserved Tom, and soon his sheer ebullience round the famous galleried coaching hotel with its affluent, city-dressed men and elegant travelling women unfroze Tom too. The richly laden tables in glossy rooms were a new world, yet not too overwhelming for the boys with Harry Bromley to ease their entry into this totally strange life. Benny was vibrant with the love of it all, and of the exciting city streets; and when at length they answered to Jos's prompting and settled down to a mufflered sparring session in the stables, Benny, out of sheer joy, gave Tom one of the fastest bouts he had ever had. Still, Harry and Jos were pleased to see Tom kept the pace, much heavier and taller though he was, and he was breathing little more than normally at the end of a long round of bewildering speed.

As the little crowd left the stables finally, Benny led Tom away and behind Jos and Harry and some of Harry's sporting friends. Still cherry-cheeked from the mock-furious sparring, he was unwontedly solemn. In his usual mannerly way Tom had just thanked him for the bout and Benny had then drawn him a little apart: "See, Tom," and he held up his hard fists and declared with solemn emotion, "that's what we've got, that few others have got - and what's in them? Well, it's the only chance we have of that," and he waved in a comprehensive gesture at the lantern-glowing, richly-endowed, gleamingly-affluent coaching inn.

"You'll reach that, Benny. You'll go far."

"Thee too, Tom - to the very top, I reckon."

"I intend to." Tom's voice was all calm assurance, unswaggering.

"I wouldn't like to get in thy way." Benny laughed, but he meant it.

****

A mile-long valley opening in serene flat Cheshire fields widened at length into a vast shallow bowl, a natural stadium. This Sunday morning it held comfortably several hundreds of men already in a state of high excitement from watching (and wagering heavily on) wrestling and cudgelling matches, cockfights and foot races earlier in the morning all along the valley. A deal of money had changed hands and now losers wagered recklessly, as losers do, to recover losses and winners gambled high and happily with the other fellow's money. All were impatient, the roped-off ring by its emptiness seeming to draw into itself massively increasing charges of fight-lust and of greed for golden sovereigns.

A rising and falling roaring expressed their impatience that the fighters come to the ring and the roar rose to one steady note, as of one great voice, at the sound, at last, of jingling harnesses from a procession of coaches driven fast in the direction of the stadium. These pulled in a little way up the valley to form a circle, and within it Tom Bradbury stripped to the waist and fastened Harry Bromley's "silk" as a belt about his middle. On his feet he tied light dancing shoes, lacing them firmly round his insteps.

A note of urgent conference, estimating him, followed him through the lane formed by the spectators' parting to give him way. There was keen scrutiny and critical appraisal of this new fighter: so tall, shapely as a statue of a Greek athlete, red hair to set off fair skin, a lord for looks; and puzzled comment: "No scrapper, yon; not a mark on him," and "Too fine: he'll last naught at all." And Tom entered the ring to only a thin cheer. While far across the bowl another human lane was forming, and here there were hearty cheers and loud, hoarse exhortations: "Come on, Jamie, fib him straight; there's nobbut a dancing master o'er yon!" Tom's opponent was of a different breed: enormously muscled; narrow, small, shaven bullet-head set on a squat pillar of a neck sloping out to vast shoulders; flattened nose; ears pounded to be like small mushrooms, his whole physique tending to understate his six feet four inches of height. Jamie Bird, fancied here in his native Cheshire to fight champions soon.

Preliminaries were few. Two umpires were named and then both men brought by their seconds to the scratch, a yard-long line scored in the centre. Brief instructions, a quick handshake and the fight was on.

The anticipatory roar as the two men squared at the scratch soon diminished into angry, impatient shouts as Jamie, his nose already bleeding from a whiplike left, with menacing growls closed near, prepared for stand-up battle. But Tom backed away, moving like a dancer but always with the left foot before the right, beautifully balanced. And on came Jamie, lashing out with massive blows that would have crushed; but they never landed. Instead, occasionally, Tom's straight left, vicious, razor-like, cut into Jamie's flattened face, splattering blood now freely flowing; and the angry crowd, the bettors growing apprehensive, yelled to Tom to stand up and fight.

The spectators were puzzled, too; most of them had seen nothing before but toe-to-toe bruising and mauling, a smashing into insensibility, the more enduring winning, and this "fighting on the retreat" was new to them. But even the angry mob backing Jamie were answered in their taunts of Tom when Jamie, by sheer bustling, forced him into a corner and on to the ropes there and furiously rained down a great flurry of blows. One or two struck Tom, who was crouching a little and swaying for balance, then he hit all his body weight flush to the jaw and Jamie's head clicked as if loosely sprung. Immediately a punch in the wind bowed him sharply forward as if he had been kicked by a horse and his arms dangled loosely with the shock of the momentary breathing paralysis. Tom took the dangling wrists and, as if the other's massive body had been a rag doll, with a twisting cross-buttocks throw pitched Jamie, limbs all askew, out of the ring, knocking the breath out of him for a second time within moments. His seconds got him but slowly to the scratch.

There could be only one ending to the fight. It came fairly quickly. Jamie fought courageously - he had a good heart - but soon he was wincing under blows that struck him like bullets. He had no fear, he did not need the taunts now mounting to spur him to fight, but he did have an odd apprehension in his bemused mind that there was before him a superhuman being who could not be struck. The eighth round saw it over; seven times Jamie had been down and he was mouthing the words again, "Stand up and...", when he saw the flicker of a fist moving towards his body. His glance wavered, a flush hit in the mouth cut off the words, and immediately with it that "horse-kick" to the belly. And spirit had gone, with strength, from Jamie. He did not come up to scratch again. There was a thin cheering. Many had lost money; few had won, and those chiefly Harry Bromley and his friends.

The story of the fight ran quickly along the coaching roads and into the inns and taverns, a story much embellished of a supernaturally gifted fighter, a demon. And the story came to Lord St Warren, who was a friend of Harry Bromley's father and who had on his estates a Welshman from fighting, wrestling Mid-Wales. A match was soon made between him and Tom for a sum of guineas that made Tom and Jos, when they heard of it, blink in disbelief, but Tom quickly accepted it. With the prize-money he had just won he kept himself, and Benny too, in full-time training with Jos. Benny he kept as his mascot and very good friend.

The Welshman, George Lewis, was a shrewder fighter than Jamie, not so vastly muscled as the general run of heavy bruiser but more athletic, faster-moving than they. Even so he lasted no longer than Jamie had done - he ran into Tom now fully-trained, razor-sharp. Within a few minutes of beginning the end was sure and George failed the scratch, as badly mauled as if he had fought for hours. The vast crowd, almost silenced by the cool "killer" violence they had witnessed in this remote valley in Mid-Wales, dispersed agog with speculation about this new fighter. George had been much fancied to fight his way south to Bristol, some time to challenge the champion; but now it was clear that this new man, Tom Bradbury, had taken his place on the long trail to the top.

Chapter 8

The next contest for Tom Bradbury had its own new importance. It was a match leading towards a fight with the best pugilists, those seen as in possible contention for the championship of England. He was matched, now jointly by Squire Bromley, Harry's father and Lord St Warren, for a sum of guineas vast even in those days of heavy gambling; the almost superstitious stories of Tom's talents had raised a new level of interest. His adversary, Henry Clarke, had little more than George Lewis, except even greater strength and more staying power. But these only served to give Tom Bradbury a few more rounds, a few more minutes, to bring the match to the same ending.

Two more fights followed from challengers in the Bristol district, men with knowledge of Jem Belcher of those parts and somewhat of Belcher's kind, more like those who would follow him in holding to the new style. "Science" was becoming the word in the rings and booths of the south. It was a word ridiculed by the backers of the old-time bruisers, but the knowledgeable saw that there were new men on the championship trail and they knew the oft-repeated stories about the fabulous young fighter from the Yorkshire Pennines.

The first fight confirmed all that they had heard and a very competent youngster was outclassed and comprehensively beaten; so that Tom, hitherto only a name and a rumour here in Bristol at the heart of English prizefighting, by this fight came clearly into view, into reckoning, and into contention with the near-best, those on the final rungs to the championship ring.

The second fight was with one such, Arthur Summers, who laid claim to lead the field from which the challengers would be drawn. He had height, over six feet and was of great strength, with wide shoulders and long reach. He and Tom Bradbury were to fight on the Downs near Bristol; early in the 1800's when the prize-ring catered for a new excitement carrying over from the wars. The stakes were high, fantastically so, the greater part being on

Summers. Wealthy merchants of the West backed Summers, while the young bucks of Harry Bromley's circle were with Harry and Tom in this exciting new adventure in pugilism - and they had Tom to train, and to provide for well, in a hunting lodge on the Squire's southern estates. Jos, trainer and second and Benny, ringmate and sparring-partner, got Tom to a pitch of fighting efficiency they knew to be different from, and way above, anything seen in the ring before.

The field was chosen for its surround of rising ground: thousands would see the fight, the fight-mad thousands of the West country. There was a new high excitement as the coaches bearing the fighters and their partners approached, and the cheering which greeted them had a strange, high, screaming note that intensified as the fighters entered the ring.

Preliminaries were brief. Time was called and the fighters were roared up to the scratch. There was a moment of silence while all eyed and judged the two men. Wagers flowed again - more still on Summers, who was inches the taller and heavier, more muscular in build; a giant making Tom look ordinary. But others, better judges, saw Tom's shoulders, as wide as the other's but sloping. They saw, too, and pointed out to each other that Tom stripped bigger than when he was clothed, the mark of an athlete; a few wagers were quietly made against the main flood and the match was on.

Summers had learned to move quickly. He was far beyond the old toe-to-toe slogging, a matter of sheer endurance of splintered bone and pulped flesh, and yet he had the terrifying strength for this. Coupled with a fair amount of skill it had brought him far and he moved confidently and briskly into action, striking hard at his opponent as he came willingly to meet him. But the sledgehammer blows fell on air and Summers was blankly amazed. It was as if his slight-seeming opponent had suddenly disappeared. His amazement became open-mouthed from a straight left to the wind. His arms dropped to the blow and he got a stinging clip over the ear. It was almost impertinent, and there was a ripple of laughter from the crowd and an answering gleam of amusement in Tom's eyes. Hot rage flooded in Summers, but he was no fool and it was with a controlled fury that he drove Tom into a corner. But Tom, with a finesse in a feint that was beyond Summers' experience, moved leftwards out of it, leaving Summers sideways on to get two wicked punches that split flesh as if they had been delivered with metal-clad knuckles. One blow to the eye shocked Summers into immobility and Tom stepped up to him, put a foot behind and threw him heavily to the ground... neat and competent wrestling.

The first round had shocked the crowd almost as much as it had Summers, but still they roared him on and he came up to scratch again, still in good shape. He was careful now; he was a courageous fighter and very strong, cleverer than most, and he pressed Tom hard, raining blows so as to compel the other into defence, blows to the forehead which badly bruised the guarding forearms. But he rarely landed anything telling and occasionally, in a rage of frustration, he left himself open - once too often. Tom stepped in to show himself as skilful a wrestler as he was a boxer, a particularly neat cross-buttocks throw making it clear to the crowd that there could be only one end to this match. They

53

appeared to realise this as one man and the great number who had backed Summers began to jeer.

The fight had gone into the eighth round and Summers was fighting desperately. Finally he tried to crush his maddening opponent in a bear-hug, only to have his grasping fists held and a shoulder thrust into his chest. A quick, fluent heave and Tom threw him out of the ring. Cheers rang thinly from the crowd, but louder were bitter jeers for Summers, loud and harsh. Shaken as he was, he was seized with a murderous rage and he sprang to his feet to vault back into the ring. Tom, the wrestling fall making the end of a round, was returning to his corner, to the laughing Benny and the toothlessly-grinning Jos, when there was a sudden flash of alarm in their faces and Benny, who had been squatting to make a knee for Tom, jerked upright, pointing and calling out a warning. Summers, now in the ring again and silent-footed in the grass, was rushing down on Tom, who was able only to half-turn into the assault. Summers struck him with all his remaining strength full on the jaw, and as Tom was falling struck him again, and with this made him crash heavily, dead weight on to a ring-post which met him fully in the temple, splinteringly, sickeningly. He fell unconscious at Benny's feet, fell as one dead, so that Benny stood stockstill, aghast; but Jos jumped into the ring and, eyes afraid, turned Tom over on to his back. Tom's eyes were half-open, but there was no life in them. Yet he began to breathe hard for a moment or so, then this breathing became rapid and shallow, and this again became straining with vomiting – straining since Tom had eaten little before the fight. Harry Bromley and his friends, with Benny, struggled mightily to give Tom and Jos some room and air as the ring was filled with a surging, screaming mob of infuriated supporters now raining blows on Summers and his seconds. The packed, raging mob made passage difficult for a surgeon, a doctor of the Bromleys, but his servant swung an efficient cudgel and made way for him. There was little the surgeon could do immediately but he got Tom, deathly unconscious now, into Harry Bromley's coach and away.

Weeks later the same doctor, accompanied by a specially commiss-ioned London surgeon at Harry Bromley's particular request, examined Tom at Jos's gymnasium. Only Benny and Jos, with Harry Bromley attended; waiting, talking little, in the coachway arch outside the gymnasium. They were soon called in and the consultant surgeon pronounced, "He is cured of a small fracture."

"Is he a well man again?" demanded Harry and with him Benny blurted out, "Will he fight again?"

The surgeon curtly answered, "Yes – to both of you. That is, if he wants to fight again – but the doctor might not be so quickly to him, should there be a next time and there is no telling what damage there was done behind the bone." He was very abrupt and seemed out of temper; his colleague looked anxiously at him, and with some reason. During the examination Tom had been vilely rude, answering the surgeon with something near to contempt, ridiculing his comments and with surliness obeying requests to be seated for examination. Only with difficulty had Harry's doctor persuaded his London colleague to continue when, as the exam-ination became a little prolonged, Tom had sneeringly asked,

"Shall I send for the nearest bloody farmer to look at it? Mend me or an animal quicker nor thee, I wager," and "Bloody well hasten thyself. Bromley'll no pay more for time."

The two surgeons wasted little time when they pronounced their findings, just a few words: "severe concussion... small fracture... thin skull bone in temporal region... always possibility of some damage to brain tissue, just there. Unguessable, that." Then they departed, with goodbyes to all. Tom did not even turn round to remark their going.

There was a considerable constraint on all remaining, but at length Harry Bromley asked, in the kindest manner, "Perhaps you had best leave fighting a while, Tom?"

The reply was sour: "I'll thank ye to leave moithering to women. I've enough of that at home."

Benny and Jos looked askance at each other, but remained silent. Harry, with an effort, replied politely enough, "Very well. I will wait until Jos tells me you are ready again," and receiving no reply, he left, beckoning Benny and Jos to the door with him. There he handed to Jos a small bag of sovereigns and said, "I have learned that you had no share of the money we managed to get on the fight?"

"'Tis so," replied Jos sadly. "Tom did give us a little but he begrudged it, like. So we asked no more. And," he added, "he used to be such an open-handed young fellow." He stopped there as Tom, dressed again, approached, pushed past them and with a surly, "I'll get me gone," hurried away. "Open-handed," Jos picked up his earlier remark, "and the nicest-spoken lad I ever saw in my life, and always a smile."

Tom Bradbury was still entitled to challenge the best; his last fight had not been held against him. His rapid smooth rise strengthened his claims to fight at least the middle best.

He was matched with a middle-order fighter, a giant, young but a mauler and bruiser of the old style. He was a Manchester journeyman, so the fight was arranged to take place in a valley on the lower Pennine moors in Lancashire, way out from the attentions of the reeve's men. The crowd was less partisan than at previous contests; both men were from the same region. And when the coaches bearing the fighters drew near the cheering was impartial enough. But for the party accompanying Tom Bradbury the cheering was but little stimulating. Whereas previous such journeys had been exciting, adventurous, all singing and laughing, this was sombre somehow, a journey of growling, murderous remarks by Tom.

Tom was first out of the coach at the match-ground, and he was ready-stripped. "You," he curtly ordered Benny, "come on." To Jos, to Harry Bromley and his friends, he said nothing, but just strode away to the ring. He was almost jigging with impatience as he stood to the scratch for the brief, rough, introductory formalities, and at the call "Set to" he furiously attacked, both fists flailing, to be punched straight off his feet by a branch-like left arm. Returning to his corner for the round he ordered Benny, offering a knee, out of the ring and raging, shouted to his opponent to "Come up to scratch!"

The fury of Tom's renewed attack held the other cautious for a while, and Tom's reputation had come before him, but his blows were automatic, just a rapid pounding with no feinting subtlety, no skill in approach, and the Manchester man with his long reach easily held off the attack. And soon he had the measure of an opponent he had been trained to respect, but who was showing here little more than a fairground-booth-bruiser's skill. Realising this, he began the merciless demolition of a once-feared fighter, until the contest became nothing more than a thrashing, round after round, and the end came with the crowd almost silent.

Tom was led away, a butchered mess, his handsome face pulped and his eyes hard with the bitterness of humiliation. Harry Bromley hurried to his side as he strode off to the coach and tried to say the comforting thing, a consoling word, but Tom merely snarled at him, "I'll fight not for thee, nor for anybody again." He gestured dismissively. "Let me get home."

Chapter 9

Tom Bradbury and Reuben Platt, the one remaining friend of his schooldays, were, at evening, walking down from the moor and on to Greenfield. At Nook Steer, the village's moor boundary, the steep lane down which they walked deepened and opened on its left into a small common. Here a group of millworkers "idle" from a stopped mill engine were playing pitch and toss. The betting was not high, so the banter of the game was jovial and good-humoured as the coins were tossed into the air, "Tanner I 'eads 'em," a frequent challenge.

"Flamming 'em, Tom," Reuben declared assuredly but quietly, so as not to be heard by the tossers.

"What dost mean, flamming 'em?" Tom demanded, but less quietly - he had no mind to be discreet for the benefit of millworkers.

Nevertheless Reuben answered him - he was describing a cheating. "Thrower puts them as he fancies on his thumb back, calls 'em so, then sends 'em up rocking and they looks to be spinning. Up they goes - 'eads, say - and so they come down, and stays so, if the ground is soft and they don't bounce."

Tom, curious, drew near, as did a group of five tatterdemalion wanderers. After a throw or two a new tosser took the coins, but he threw them inexpertly and one coin fell into the torn brim of a stranger's hat. "A halfpenny dropped into thy hat," the thrower said and the other denied it. An altercation quickly flared and the thrower appealed to Tom and Reuben.

"I know naught of it," Tom declared.

"Come on. Tha knows bloody well."

"I know naught o' the sort."

The others crowded round. "Give him his ha'penny or we'll knock your bloody hat off and get it," one shouted to the little group of wanderers.

"Let one step nigh," Tom snarled, in sheer awkwardness. There was no movement. This bristling red giant, his more than six feet of height towering over the diminutive millworkers, was well known. In his early forties he was steel-cord strong, powerful as a bull. Tom held his ground in silence until he felt to have mastered the little crowd. Then, without let, he took off the stranger's hat and flung the coin into the middle of the tiny common. After this he strolled away, scowling but satisfied.

Reuben, hastening by his side, looked sideways and up and caught the flicker of a mirthless smile turn upwards the other's set mouth. "What did tha do that for?" Reuben asked.

"I like to make folk know their place."

"Tha likes to make enemies," Reuben commented drily. "And tha'rt a bloody genius at it."

"And what does that mean?"

Reuben answered obliquely: "They say you tangled up with the 'Emeralders' up on the cut." Reuben was referring to Irish "navigators" working on the new Holmfirth-Huddersfield road. They were wild men and lawless, so much so that the women of the district had banded themselves together into a "Society" to protect each other. Few men would tangle with them, and though their very presence was a challenge, it was one so far never taken up - except by Tom Bradbury. In some gossip in his father's inn, there had been a tale of a mad exploit by some of the younger Irishmen jumping, for wagers, across the mouth of a mine shaft sunken in the hillside, and which had been disclosed by the road-cutting.

Tom described it in answer to Reuben's avid questioning as he had seen it himself. "Aye! Bloody daft they are. A good jump," he answered laconically. "Bad landing. Clay."

"Is it the drop they say it is, Tom?"

"About two hundred feet."

"Christ! They say some missed it!"

"Three, for sure. Daft and wild they are - like monkeys."

"Challenged thee to it, they do say?" Reuben prodded.

"Aye. I'd heard the tale up at the Moorcock. Didn't believe it. Went to see for myself and there were one or two 'Pats' about; four, in fact."

"Dogged thee on, did they? Mocked thee?"

"Oh, aye," Tom answered with indifference. "Wanted to fight, but if I'd taken one, any one, I'd have got the four."

"You got away, then - no trouble?"

"I'd a shotgun."

"And tha'd have used it," Reuben declared with certainty.

"Aye. Even so, they came up to the inn later - three of them, anyway - but I cleared them off," Tom growled. "There were some stockings missing from the line our washing-woman put out. I reckon they took them. Just let me find out."

"Any chance this is a paying-back for last backend, Tom?"

"If so be, it's a poor one." Tom chuckled grimly. "They swore they'd kill me for it afore they went back to Ireland."

They spoke of a wild act of Tom's, a "joke" he had called it to himself at the time, but it was a joke of malevolence, humourless, like the man himself. Tom, coming down half-drunk from a moorland inn, had had to pass a hutment, hardly a house, roughly timber-framed, roughly roofed too, with thick turves or sods. It sheltered for the night fifteen or so navvies from the new roadworks and Tom, in typically hurtful mischief, used his great strength to drag out a corner post, so as to bring the heavy roof and timbers crashing down on the sleepers within.

None was at all seriously hurt, none killed, but the navvies had been heard to swear they would have Tom's life for it. But no more had come of it since its happening late in the previous summer and it was all half-forgotten - certainly by Tom, though some would say the Irish were bad forgetters of a grudge, and that Tom had best look out for himself before these particular Emeralders were due to depart for Ireland. Reuben went so far as to remind Tom of this, but all he got was a casual, "Naught to fear there," total indifference in words and tone.

Admiring of Tom's unconsciously arrogant self-confidence, Reuben nevertheless felt mischievously inclined to needle that assurance. And with a casualness to match Tom's he introduced, with complete indifference, half-yawningly, a new topic into the conversation. "They do say," he said, "that the 'crowner' at the inquest on that baby - you know, down at the King William last week."

"No, I don't know," a dour, rude rejoinder.

"Well," Reuben persisted, "they do say the lass with the baby were right bonny, worked up at the farm on the brow, but not from these parts. They say..."

"They! They! They!" Tom angrily interrupted. "Who the hell are 'they'? And what's this to do with me or thee?"

"I ne'er said it had," Reuben answered hastily, a little startled by the other's vehemence.

"Well!" Tom snarled. "If thou'st naught better to do than tittle-tattling like a wench, then I have. Let's get my errand done and thee gone." And he gestured dismissively and strode away, the truth to tell, doing so glad to get rid of Reuben. A few moments agone he had made up his mind to submit to a ceaseless goading within him, and he hastened long-striding towards Wessenden Head.

Chapter 10

Thrusting hard, as might a spurred horse, at times even running a little, Tom Bradbury hastened the lower reaches of the Dovestone valley, following close the brook draining down here from the far Wessenden Head Moor. Within minutes though, he knew that this was not a pace to be maintained and he turned out for the high road to his master's house. With some stealth he approached the rear of the house and the stables, and here demanded of a young groom a horse, saddled and bridled. He met with furious resistance, only momentarily offered as Tom advanced, scowling, ferocious, fists forward. The youngster complied, grumbling, "Tha stands thy own corner if t'gaffer gets to know," and led forth at length a fine bay.

"He'll not get to know unless you tell him, and God help you if you do that," Tom snarled, and with a clatter he was away, to the burnplatters' and gypsies' communes and encampments at Wessenden Head.

So, well horsed as he was, Tom went forward confidently, without fear. Afoot, he would have called in at his old home for a gun, for though most in the encampments on the remote plateau were gypsies – and rough enough they were – there were also rogues, mumpers, vagabonds and worse; quite literally savages, wild, unkempt, filthy, dressed as savages, many even in skins; savages in behaviour but living, perforce, in some sort of amity with the gypsies.

Tom rode fast along the sides of the majestic peaks of Aldermans Hill. This eased down to the miles-spreading moors with their sombre colours fading in the great distance, their far horizons tinily castellated with the roofs of remote hamlets. In the innermost reaches of the final gentle slopes and plateaux, so far distant from the roads and habitations of man as to be in a kind of desert island in the moors, were the encampments. There were waggons, raggedly sheeted; shabby, unpainted caravans; turf-roofed shebeens, mud-plastered; tents; even caves hollowed out of the near hillside.

Tom rode the old road, spurring his horse, himself spurred, until he reached the brow of a hill something less than a mile out from the camp. There he halted, took out his gamekeeper's telescope and carefully scrutinised the endlessly-moving denizens of the camp, that was a little less squalid-seeming at the distance. Indeed in the evening sun, April-bright, the gypsy caravans seemed to be bedecked with coloured ribbons and green boughs. This was what Tom had come, devil-driven, to investigate; driven so, he angrily admitted to himself, by no more than the words of a braggart. Two nights gone, in his father's taproom, a pedlar, with his tray of bobbins of thread and cotton and dress-tape, had held older men agape with his account of a couple of days and nights spent "up yon" with the burnplatters. He had listened as they spoke of cheating the "gayjos", the English village-folk; robbing them, selling gewgaw rubbish, telling fortunes. They had spoken, too, of weddings as they plaited their baskets from down-stream withies and fashioned and plaited on the besoms made from moorland rushes.

The older men had guffawed as he told them that some sorts would count themselves wed by simply stepping over a besom hand in hand, others by pissing in the same bucket. They would eat a cake that contained blood and sweat and hair of them both, and all the gypsy men would work to build a turf-and-pole hut for them. And the boy went on to say that a wedding was coming up. Here Tom Bradbury began to pay a closer attention; he had been on the point of threatening the boy with a clip over the ear for going on chattering so before grown men, but now he listened.

Bill's o' Jack's at the turn of the century

"So whiles the men are building the girl sits still on the ground outside her family home, does so with her black frizzy hair" – so the boy described it – "drawn round her face, her head quite still, bowed down." This showed that she was "tokened".

Ofttimes since, this picture had come vividly into Tom's imaginings. Was it she? Martha? "Black, frizzy hair?" But they all had black, frizzy hair, he said to himself. And yet he knew that he had to find out; and here he was.

Still asaddle, he waited. Nothing special in the random movements of the tiny figures, men and women and children in the spaces and ginnels criss-crossing their crazy "village". Was he too late? It seemed so, and yet there was an impression of excitement in the milling movements; then suddenly the movement stopped; spaces were cleared; at length there came the faint screech of a fiddle and a short procession emerged from among the hutments and caravans. Even at the distance and using his telescope, he could see that a white-clad woman, led by a man, was veiled, but it was not she; not Martha. This woman was tall, taller than the man; and she walked somewhat stooped, whereas Martha walked straight, with something of the arrogance that goes with beauty and a short temper – invitation and danger, both.

Tom had stood in his stirrups to see the better. Now he sank back in relief, only to feel at once disconcerted by a faintness and a dizziness. "By God," he swore to himself, "you've got it bad this time, Tom Bradbury."

He had to make a deliberate effort to compose himself; then, as he was about to put a spur to his horse, he caught a glimpse of a figure far off at the very rearmost of the caravans and huts. "Well I'm damned!" Tom was astonished. "Eliphalet!" No mistaking that odd figure, so narrow at the shoulder that his long coat, almost like a cloak, billowed out to the ankles, so as to give him an unmistakable pear-shape.

At the distance Eliphalet with his weak, pink, albino eyes had not seen Tom, though Tom was, on his horse and on the crest of a hillock, plain to see. But another had seen, peering round the end of a covering caravan, and a hand reached out to pull back Eli into cover. And the other was Martha.

Tom hesitated only momentarily. He remembered that Eli had said once that he did some sort of trade with the platters, whisky and that. And Tom turned his horse and was off at a gallop. Eliphalet was no concern of his – never saw him these days, anyway.

Within a few short paces the long-striding horse was checked. Three platter youths were straddling the bridle-path, as if to bar passage; but they soon scattered as Tom, whip held high, spurred his horse at a leap into them and rode on without a backward glance. But even that short encounter had raised in Tom an explosive fury, way beyond the trivial nature of the incident; and this fury seemed to burst into redness behind his eyes, to daze him and to cause him to sway in his saddle. Clear vision seemed to leave him, and yet he could see... but blankly, somehow. The high bracken to each side, still yellow from last autumn's downturn, was not sharp in his focus. All seemed a smooth blur as if long beaches of golden sand stretched to the sides and on to the horizon, and the low trees and scanty bushes were only shadows on the smooth gold. But soon all became defined: the golden bracken in patches on the olive-green heather, and the bright ling.

A puzzlement annoyed Tom, and this deepened as the tingling began again. It had happened twice before and Tom had not so remarked it, but both times it had followed outbursts of fury. His right arm from shoulder to the skin on his very fingertips tingled, for a while almost unbearably, then fading to nothing... gone; and with it Tom's notice of it, for instantly a quick remembered picture of Eli way out among the caravans flicked into his mind. But only for a moment. Tom, as previously, dismissed the thought of Eli as no concern of his. But Tom was very much a concern of Eli's, and at that moment too, as Martha was asking Eli, there hidden in the sheltering caravan, just what he wanted of her.

Eli had just had in mind a little mischief-making, perhaps to baulk "that Tom Bradbury", when he had been saying to Martha to keep out of the reach-and-touch of him; that in a village alehouse Tom had been boasting to his crony Reuben that one time he would have her, and had sworn it so. That was an exaggeration by Eli, and he had been preparing to embroider the story when Martha had pulled him into the cover of the caravan.

"There's that red pig, Tom Bradbury, up yon now." She spoke in a low, choking voice and it was as if a virulent hatred tightened her throat. "Thou needst not tell me what that bastard might say. Twice he's stopped me on the old road; but there were some Pats near, both times. I wish I'd a brother or a man to my side to put a 'chiv' into him."

Eli, surprised and intrigued by the violence, real and murderous, in the words, probed, rat-like and opportunist: "None to take your part?"

"Oh, aye, if it came to the 'Hey', but most keep shy o' yon. When he's been moithering for rent up here, and he's been threatened, he's threated back that he'd have the constables and the military to us." Her voice was bitter now with loathing. "And I reckon he would; and enjoy it."

Eli picked up his quarry again. "So, none to side with you against him, except, maybe, too late?"

Martha, who knew what the "too late" meant, muttered, "Just so."

"Well, maybe you can take your own part and at the same time get money to buy, perhaps, some o' the ragged-arses," he jerked his head towards the huts and the caves, "buy them to your side."

"Money!" Martha was bitterly scornful. "Money! What money might I have? And dost think I'd let them," she jerked a thumb over her shoulder, "have a sight of it, if I had? But thou'st something in mind?" She looked with ancient shrewdness at Eli.

"Aye, like this." Eli was urgent: "Tha'll ne'er get a knife into Tom Bradbury; but tha can hurt him just as sore. Listen, canst steal?"

Martha was taken aback by the abrupt question, but she saw that Eli was in earnest, and by way of answer she reached out and
62

half-turned him, pushed him a little and said, "See if Bradbury's gone. He was up the far hill."

Eli peered, then, "So far as I can see," and turned to find Martha smiling. "Here," she said, and handed him his laced purse and gunmetal watch. "Bloody hell!" Eli was astonished. "When did you get them?"

"Just now. And," she spoke proudly, "I could clear a house out as quick and as quietly, get me in it. What's in your mind, Eli?"

Eli answered obliquely, "Tom Bradbury. Hast a right grudge theer? Dost want to pay him out for his moithering; or art afeard of him?"

"Afeard of him? Aye, in a way. To me, he's a devil, a real one." Martha, of her kind ruled by age-old superstitions, made an odd little gesture as if to seek protection, as another might cross herself.

"Then this is for thee. Get at him roundabout. Listen: Tom Bradbury's meanest sod i' these parts. It's surely meant for him, that old saying, 'He's short arms and long pockets'. Well, he gloats on getting his father's brass one day. There's a fair bit of it, sovereigns mostly and some silver, and I know where it's kept. Tom, when he were ale-taken once and me right close to him then," Eli scowled a little, "told me where it is always. Threatened me later he'd half-kill me if e'er I spoke on't. And so far, I'm telling thee... the only one."

"Why doesn't tha take it, Eli?" asked Martha shrewdly.

"I'd be no good in a strange house, at least up the stairs where this is kept. I don't see good e'en by daylight."

That was fair, but Martha then said, "Suppose, since I'd be taking it, I'd give thee none?"

"Then I'd tell," and that settled that and Martha began to ponder. The rights and wrongs of theft had no part in her thinking. All her life she had seen, and been taught, that stealing and cheating and "conning" were just means of livelihood. To gain was all. Property, others' property, was there to take. Just avoid being caught, that was all. Her father had taught her to steal and to pick pockets as a gayjo father might have taught his child to play games. Martha's mind was not invested by such thoughts but by the feelings within herself, of herself. Amoral of property and money rights, she was fiercely, deadly moral of her own person and of her relations with youths and men of her gypsy kind. Since she was a little girl of eleven or twelve she had had the attentions of men. She had had beauty then already, but more, a mysterious extra quality of sexual attractiveness that had intensified as she had come into womanhood. And as she had learned to know herself, she had gone about much in the company of her menfolk, now away: father and uncle, one dead, the other in gaol. Still she had remained immaculate, virginal. And it was this oddly evident air of virginity with so much dark beauty and swinging, unconsciously provocative stride that was irresistible, maddeningly irresistible, to one such as Tom Bradbury.

The thought of him offended Martha deeply, defiled her; the raw lust and the crude obscenities of their last encounter, the one saved for her by the chance appearance of the Irish navigators, were felt almost as a physical manhandling and now, as she spoke to Eli, she cringed at the memory and crouched a little, a low tiny snarl of animal rage curling her lips tight. "Right," she whispered vibrantly. "Tell me what to do."

"It'll be easy enough," Eli assured her. "But we've talked here long enough. See me Thursday at just this time, at the bottom of the road from the Cock Crowing Stone. It's out of sight of here."

Eli was careful to take a circuitous route away from Wessenden Head but he had nothing to fear; Tom Bradbury was galloping away, on another errand while he was in these parts. He felt a bounding exaltation that Martha was not the bride in that little procession, a crazy exaltation that raised in him a desire to parade his sense of triumph in a show of power. And soon he turned his horse from the wide Holmfirth cart-road into a narrow by-lane, at the end of which stood a simple, poor-looking cottage. Tom reined his horse with a clatter on the rough cobbles and shouted authoritatively, "Come out, Jamie Bradbury. I want thee."

The wide unpainted door opened for three people to appear. One, slightly leading the others, was of such outrageous ugliness as not to be seen immediately as human: pig-faced, bristle-headed, nose twisted and broken, ears gristly relics. At his shoulder a grinning replica, without teeth and a youngish woman of some peasant good looks, brother and sister, stood silent while the leader, Jamie, made a smirking attempt at ingratiatingly familiar address: "Why, Tom, hast come to call it off, for us Bradburys, like?"

"You're no bloody kin o' mine and well you know it. You be at Pontefract, Tuesday. Dost hear? As I tell thee."

Jamie's face changed expression to a scowling frightfulness as he said, "I take no bloody orders from thee, Tom Bradbury. I'll hearken to the constables. Tha'rt nowt. Only tha'rt a bigger bloody poacher than any of us. Tha shouldst stand Pontefract before us'n."

Tom fumbled with his whip, then stopped quite still; he had had a flash of memory of the bruiser in the Oldham pub long ago. He had sworn to return to him, but never did. And here was just such another, Jamie Bradbury. Tom felt a flush of rage spark within him, then, sickeningly, the flattening again of the scene before him: the cottage flat, the three expectant faces flat and the tingling beginning in his arm again. Hatred and defiance showed in all the three, not least in the woman's face. She Tom had totally ignored, though he had known her well enough once. Tom, as if recognising unconsciously the cause of his dreadful unease, flung away from the little group who were causing the fury to rise within him, turned his horse and fled, fear in his eyes – leaving the Bradburys astonished. "That bastard afeared of us?" Jamie wondered aloud.

By now the late March evening was darkening fast and Eli made haste to get off the open moors and the hillsides, with their foot-tangling tussocks and snare-like heather roots. Stumbling often in his haste, he stopped only when he reached the smoother lower slopes of Aldermans Hill, where he paused as if to cogitate. He looked out over darkness, and darker moors; here and there shone the tiny yellow light of a candle in a farm or a cottage window. Way out, a mile or so, the low hill of Wimberry Stones Brow curved against a southern sky taking a little light yet from the west. Through Longendale, Glossop, over Hayfield to Chapel-en-le-Frith; all of fifteen miles of a walk and hard going. Citywards? Manchester? Beg a lift on a cotton wagon? No, best not to have his journey known. And for that, to be away well before dayrise. So Eli's thoughts ran, and now he was satisfied and walked on, stooped in thought, his two rat-like upper teeth gleaming a little in a smile of anticipation. Away then, to see the man from Chapel; rest up by day and return for nightfall, none knowing whence he came. Home first for a string bag of food, just bread and cheese, put up for him by a mother who long since had ceased to ask questions.

He was ready for an early morning start after a short rest, and no need to call anywhere for so much as a bite. He could water at the moorland streams mostly out of all sight and his tiny figure, only showing at odd times, was indistinguishable so far out in remote moors.

Chapter 11

Eli had met Martha as he had said, out of sight of the encampment and far from the Holmfirth Road, the moorlanders' road, and he was instructing her. "Monday night it must be, then. No-one e'er goes in the Bill's o' Jack's on a Monday - no money, I reckon. The house is ne'er locked or bolted. Now there's a chap'll be there to help thee, needs be. Box, tha sees, might be too heavy for a lass."

Martha was suspicious: "What chap? How much sharing is there to be?"

"He's noan o' these parts and he'll want naught but a sovereign or two. Maybe not that. I'll tell thee. Mindst thou that inquest on a babby, t'other week?" Martha shook her head and Eli said, "It were in t'paper."

"Paper!" Martha was scornful. "At sevenpence a time?"

"Well, he's brother to the lass. He'd give aught to get even wi' Tom Bradbury after the showing-up his sister got - they put her away. She wouldn't tell, but this felly knows it to be Bradbury starts it all."

"Why don't he take it out on Bradbury, then?"

"He knows he couldn't lace Bradbury. More likely get a hiding hisself. Though he's a big fellow - was in the wars, I reckon; he carries a big pistol, army-like, and he knows his mark."

"How come tha knows him?"

"He makes hisself known to me. Claims he's a tapeseller or some such. He'd known that Tom and me were once together and that there'd been a fratching between us." Eli's tone suddenly changed; his words ripped out, cracking like a whip, viciously. "I'd go further than any one on you to get Bradbury. I'd take his bloody life, let alone his money."

"Why not you and this stranger-fellow, then?"

"Talking to him I gets the idea. The money'll be Tom's for sure; he spoke of it as his. The old chap'll ne'er spend it."

"He's a good'un at claiming what's not his, that red pig," muttered Martha. "Claiming rent for land not his'n and charging for brush-broom as if he owned it."

"Tha can take his brass, then and ne'er give it a thought. This chap helping would ha' noan of it. Wouldn't know how to steal, he said. But when I tell him this second time, he were on it like a shot."

"That's settled, then. I'm on."

Eli now showed her a little plan of the inn. "Take mark o' that, the back door, facing Oldham way somewhat. It'll sure be open for thee. Our helper'll make it so, going out, like as a customer to the piss-stones on that side. Thou to be in the plantation. Go wi' care, that's all, and all should be easy."

"And where will thou be?"

"I'll stay on the broad path on the hillside, and that's where I want you to be, Monday night, dead opposite, as soon as 'tis dark. All three of us for a start. When it's all o'er - and tha'll ne'er ha' money so easy - I'll let you both know the coast is clear and off we go, o'er the Pots and Pans. Share out there, get rid o' the box, split up and away."

The stranger met Eli at Ravenstones, across the valley from the inn. They came up through the plantation of young trees at the far side and over the road to the hillside road, to the meeting place. Eli then walked alone up this road, some impatient doubt in him as Martha had not yet arrived. He soon met her, though and they returned, coming on the stranger to surprise him, making him jump in the dark. "Here's Martha, who'll do the job." Eli introduced them in a whisper. "Now, hold on a two-three minutes," and he moved, shadow-like, away.

When he returned, he spoke again in a whisper: "Across to the plantation now, Martha. Bill's on his own; he'll not hear you through them thick walls. And thee go down," turning to the man, "quiet-like a way down to the wide road theer, then come up ordinary-like and go in as a customer. Main door tha can see." A glimmer of candlelight from within just outlined the door. "Stairs face thee on thy left hand. Through past them to the back door. Soon as maybe, open it to Martha. She'll hear the latch. Bill tha'll find stretched out on a settle just inside, near corner, the room on the left. He always bides there with a pot when it's quiet-like. And he's noan long before he's off to bed." Then he grabbed the others by the arms. "Hush now." His whisper was urgent. There were voices from down the old Holmfirth Road, voices soon sounding loud, rollicking voices, as of men with plenty of ale in them; voices cheerfully shouting oaths and obscenities as they passed the inn.

Tom Bradbury's name was among the oaths and abuse, but they passed on. They knew that Tom was not at the inn. They had seen him in the village near the shops whiles since, going the other way. Tom had seen them, too. Earlier that evening he and his old mate Reuben had left the Bill's o' Jack's to walk the couple of miles down to the village shops at Roadend, to get candles and some provisions for the old man. It was still a little light as Tom and Reuben neared the village, where they came upon three loutish fellows clowning and pushing each other about. These had mockingly and impudently shouted out to Tom, passing, "Thee there. Which bloody road to Holmfirth? If tha knows aught."

Tom most strangely held his temper because an instinct had made him afraid to lose it, and he answered reasonably and walked on; but to Reuben he said, "Did'st notice that two turned their backs to me when I spoke, Reuben?"

"Aye, they seemed to me hiding, like."

"I'm sure that's the lot – Pats they are – who were causing trouble up at my old fellow's. Stole the stockings, I reckon. I don't like it, them going up past the pub." But they had reached the shops now and Reuben, who had been merely accompanying Tom "for the walk", turned off to make his way up the steep track at the foot of the far Pots and Pans to his home at Primrose, close to the by-road to St Chad's, Saddleworth Church.

The "Pats" made good ground on the higher road out of the village, passed the Bill's o' Jack's without halt and soon their shouting, singing and cheerful abuse of each other dwindled to whispers and finally were lost, to leave the moors silent as they were black once more.

Satisfied, Eli gave the word: "Go. Both go." Without the slightest sound Martha, bare of foot, was gone. Her confederate, keeping to the grassy bank to make his footfall quiet too, cautiously covered a hundred yards or so, then turned on to the road and strode his normal gait back to enter the wide front doorway, still, in spite of the darkness, with its door a little ajar.

As Eli had said, the stranger found old Bill Bradbury reclining on a settle in the right hand room. Staring a little in surprise, Bill got up: "Tha'rt travelling through?" he asked mildly. At the stranger's nod he went on, "Aye, there's noan o' these parts comes to see me, Monday. Tha'll want a drink, I reckon?" Again a nod and "Aye." "One like that?" Bill asked, gesturing towards a big blue pot half full of ale which stood by the settle, ready to his hand as he had his evening rest there.

"Will do nicely," laconically. Truth to tell, the big stranger was half-choked by emotion, by the frightening dishonest nature of his errand there, that and a deep repugnance to steal from this mild, kind-eyed old man. Only with an effort, and by remembering that Tom Bradbury was the one to injure, did he harden his mind. He held his ground, paid his shot and took a long, steadying drink. Then he remembered his part and put his pot down. "I'll go out to your back while I'm here," he said.

"Down t'passage – out to your right."

And the stranger went out, making a decided rattle on the latch and leaving the door ajar.

When he returned Martha was standing by the door, back to the wall. As he re-entered the inn she moved in too, close in step, and she and the man's shadow were as one until they reached the stairs, Then she was gone, treading the solid stairway light as a down-feather, and he returned to the main room. As he entered, old Bill was tilting his head back, emptying his pot. "Well, dost want another?" and receiving no for an answer, Bill completely astonished the other by saying, "Then tha need'st not hasten. Finish thy drink proper, then let thyself out. I'm off to my bed," and ambling off, "Goodnight."

The big stranger was for a moment rigid with astonishment, aghast and still, then he hastened to the foot of the stairs and called out in an overloud voice, so as to give some warning: "Which is best road to Holmfirth, landlord?"

"Keep on going, as from the village. It's a goodly step. I'd not leave it long, if I were thee. Pull the door to, on the latch," the old man called down and trudged up the stairs again.

The man below listened intently but there was no untoward sound – just the scrape of a chamberpot on the bare wooden boards, soon the creaking of the bed, then silence. Clearly Martha had not been observed. Satisfied, the stranger took off his heavy boots and with these in hand stood waiting. Within a few minutes Martha appeared at the head of the stairs, barely visible in an indirect candlelight, and she gestured to her confederate to come up. He climbed quietly, carefully and at her sign entered a small room, facing that of the old man. He put on and laced his boots and waited again. Martha had gone.

When she had first entered Bill's bedroom Martha had located a hiding place by the flash of a tinder-box, as once she had been taught. There was a large wardrobe, forming a deep niche between its side and the windowside wall. The same glimpse showed her the bed just where Eli had said, as he had coached her in every aspect of this large, plain, Saddleworth stone house and its sparse furniture.

Now she stood in the bedroom doorway a while. Within a minute or so the old man was snoring a little so she began a patient, back-to-the-wall progression rightwards round the room, testing each floorboard before putting her weight on it. But they were solid firm and she made her way without the slightest sound to the niche. In the few minutes of her patient journey the old man had begun to snore deeply and Martha dropped to hands and knees to crawl forward, stealthily as a hunting cat, to the bedside across from the door, head to the wall. She had reached out to its deep valance when, again like a hunting cat, she froze. A voice was shouting loudly up the stairs, "Hello there, father. Are you all right?" and for all her practised self-control she uttered a tiny cry, followed by a shuddering, gasping breath of sheer terror. It was Tom Bradbury; that hated, dreadful voice! But before she could move, a hand dropped heavily on her neck, knocking her face into the ground, and then grabbed her dress at the back to haul her to her knees. The old man held her tight and in that instant Tom, lighted candle in hand, entered, to stand stock still totally amazed as the old man exclaimed, almost in a whisper, "God Almighty! It's a lass!"

Chapter 12

Tom did not hear his father's exclamation or he might have acted differently. For a moment he stared, not crediting what he saw; then fury, jealousy-fired, exploded in his mind and his face contorted into a rigid, terrifying mask. He laid down his candle-holder, the candle flame bright against the blackness of windows and doorway, and Martha in that instant wrenched herself free and dashed for the door. But Tom, straightening up, with a solid backhander as he might strike a man, knocked her sprawling across the room.

The old man, agilely enough, had jumped out of bed to pursue her and was now face to face with Tom; and what he saw there flooded him with fear: the eyes staring at him, and into which he stared, were inhuman. Tom was mindless in any human sense; the scene before him, golden-lit, was red; every figure; everything flat, unreal. The figure of his father was a jumble, swirling and flickering, of many men: Red Bradbury; opponents in his fights in the ring; the pub bruiser; the booth negro boy; his master; his schoolmasters; all as he had seen them, variously mocking, jeering, sneering, menacing. A startling tingling in his right arm caused him to look down; he held by the barrel a heavy horse-pistol that he had, unwontedly suspicious, taken from the wall in the downstairs room. He raised it deliberately and his intention was clear. The old man, voice faltering and weak with sudden panic, pleaded faintly, "Nay, Tom lad, don't," and Tom hit him full across the mouth, the heavy pistol butt mashing the lips and jaw.

It was a hurtful rather than a disabling blow and old Bill, knowing he must now defend himself, raised his fists and fought a valiant old man's best. But Tom was still wielding the pistol, only occasionally using his left hand and he struck crudely, unscientifically, seeking only to hurt and injure all those faces, and he struck mindlessly, mercilessly, as bull terriers at a downed bull. The old man struggled on, even forcing Tom back a little into the doorway so that Martha was still trapped within the room. But her heart rose from its deathly terror when, above the fury of the struggle at the door, above the cursing and the laboured gasps, there was the sound of men's footsteps on the stairs, footsteps running heavily but running, seemingly unheard by Tom, who turned only at the last moment to a storm of heavy blows to the head.

Exhausted not a little by his crazed rage as by his fighting, Tom turned to engage his new attackers. A heavy cudgel blow knocked the pistol from his grasp, insecure on a barrel slippery with blood, and forced him to fight only with his great, powerful fists. These must contend against cudgel and, infinitely more dangerous, a large spade of semi-circular blade, jagged at its edge and sharp from its digging, murderous as a battle-axe. But the swing of it was hampered somewhat by the nearness of the walls on the tiny landing and Tom fought well to force the battle on to there. He was turned there by savage cutting blows to the neck and face and driven with a thud against the facing door.

At this instant Martha made her bid to escape, bounding like a chased hare through the door. Tom's attackers checked momentarily at the sight of her, one stumbled in his surprise on the top stair and for a moment there was a tangle of falling bodies and a halt to the fighting. Martha was committed to flight and she leaped forward but Tom grabbed her by the neck as she darted past. "Let me go!" she screamed, and on that the facing door opened, no figure yet appearing. And Tom, as if jerked back into a kind of reality by that womanly scream, pulled back almost into that room. Exultingly, triumphantly, he cried, "Now, by God, you're for me!"

The door behind was now open wide. Tom never saw the blow that felled him, nor heard the words that went with it, "No more, Tom Bradbury." It was a full-armed downward swing of a heavy brass-bound army pistol, tape-bound as to its butt to make it a cudgel. A bone-cracking blow to the head and Tom went down forwards to his knees, dragging Martha down with him into the blood on the landing but in a moment releasing her. She jumped rather than ran down the stairs, past the astonished men giving her way, bloodied foot slipping a little on a lower stair and balancing hand bloody and smearing sideways a little, so that its print seemed as large as a man's.

The men on the stairs surprised by Martha stood stock still, offering no stop to her. Then they saw Tom on hands and knees, head hanging, and one cried, "Come on up again! Tom's down!" On they came again, savagely striking and Tom, some consciousness still remaining to him, struggled to his feet as once he had done in the ring, and fought on. But by now blood was spurting from arteries severed by the deadly spade, and his fighting was no more than a slow revolving with stumbling steps from stair to stair, blows driving him again and again against the stairwall so that blood smeared and ran all the way down from shoulder height: walls, handrail, side windows even, all adrip with blood. At the foot of the stairs Tom's hands dropped; he was finished, eyes closed, knees buckling to pitch him forward, and one said, "Draw him into the side room – it's never used – chance a'body comes in." And there they dragged him and left him face down, blood still pulsing slowly from him to form a great, congealing pool.

"Settle th'old fellow now." They ran upstairs into the bedroom, one going forward with spade raised and, "Now for thee," he said grimly. The old man, very very faintly hearing, raised an arm protectively against an edge-blow which severed the arm-muscle to the bone. His assailant raised the spade again, then seeing from the dreadfully mauled face and head that no more was needed, turned to ransack the house. Their gains were paltry enough – a few pounds worth of silver and copper – but little regret for that. Their primary objective lay, quiet as if in sleep, in the pantry-room there.

The intruders left, triumphant in victory over the feared Tom Bradbury. Soon afterwards the stranger, with infinite caution, left too. He found Martha and Eli where they had first met, waiting for a final word from him. "All gone. Naught to fear in there - now or ever, I reckon," he said. "I'll get me gone, Eli. And think on it well, I ne'er wants to see thee again."

70

"Nor me thee!" replied Eli with dry emphasis, and departed.

Martha, though, asked of the stranger, "Tha'rt sure there's naught to fear in there now?"

"I tell you again: I doubt either will speak again," he sombrely replied; and Martha, whose deeply ingrained instinct to thieve had been frustrated, and at one point so near to a great swag, sped across to the inn. Courageous as she was, she shunned the upstairs, but scoured around the counter-drawers and simple furniture of the main drinking-room, missing, fortunately for her, the pantry-room door behind which Tom lay. She found little but a few items of clothing, gathered these and fled, a little satisfied. She returned to their meeting-place across the roadway, but finding it deserted now, hastened over the high dark moor, back to the enveloping secrecy of her tribe.

The stranger had gone on a long journey home, first into the Ashway Valley deep beyond the inn. His first few steeply-pitching steps put up from its scrape a lapwing, its plaintive cry bringing vividly into his mind the piteous moaning of the old man back there. In their few brief moments of contact he had liked the kindly gentleness of him... and now? He strode on, mile after mile of difficult tussocky moor, keeping topside of the villages though forced, so, to cross deep ravines and fast-flowing streams. Only village dogs were aware of him and gave cry, village after village, with great intervals between each outcry; way down into the Derbyshire peaks, the hours of his journey told by barking dogs. Daylight came and the dogs, morning-wakened, ceased to cry out as the stranger made his last, infinitely weary steps into his home. He little cared, now, that he had got there. Sobbing with guilt and remorse, he was truly, to himself and to his soul, an utterly lost criminal; no pride in self left; nothing to stay here for any more.

Early morning and Bill Bradbury wakened too, to a nightmare part real: one of whirling, wounding weapons; of the menacing, murderous voice and face of his cherished son; of faces dimly recognised by injured eyes and in poor candlelight; all seen only weakly in his inward vision as his hold on life weakened. Faintly through the mists of relived terror the purpose of it all came to him, the breaching of his home, the assault upon what was his. Only this came through as he thrust out, from some deep fatherly loyalty, the memory of his son's part. Incredibly, he now arose from his bed to make an agonisingly long journey across his room and down the stairs, only long usage, and no conscious mind, leading him there. The faint, fighting notion of protecting his own moved him yet. But at the foot of the stairs, painfully reached, his body could carry the struggle no longer and he turned again, defeat accepted. His mind wandering and wondering at the strange image of a gypsy girl, he toilingly climbed, bloody of footstep, muttering in wavering bewilderment over and over, "Platter. Platter. Platter." Mumbling and slurring the word in a mouth crushed and sticky with blood, he held this puzzling memory faintly in a dying mind, and it became his last conscious thought. And so he came to his bed for the last time, to be an eternity, all of a long day and night, in dying.

Chapter 13

The Manchester Courier of April 7th 1832 reported the crime:

"On Monday evening of April 2nd one of the most diabolical murders ever committed took place at the well-known public house Bill's o' Jack's, in one of the wildest and most dreary valleys in Saddleworth on the line of the Ashton-under-Lyne and Huddersfield Road. The two inmates, the publican, 85 years of age, William Bradbury, or, as commonly called, Bill o' Jack's, and his son, Thomas, 47, were the victims of this atrocious deed.

The crime was not discovered until half-past ten o'clock the following morning, when a little girl, granddaughter of the old man, happening to call for some barm, found the two unfortunate individuals on the floor" (report so; actually William was found in bed) "weltering in blood; the walls and flags streaming with gore. With the moans of the house-dog over the victims, still alive, it was a spectacle of the most heart-rending description...

Tom, with fifteen frightful gashes, and with skull fractured, and in intense pain, died at 3.00pm on the Tuesday. The old man, not so dreadfully mangled, but injured in the face, leg and left hand, died on Wednesday morning, at 1.00am...

Relations of the deceased found that £7, and several suits of clothes were missing... taken by the murderers who, it is supposed, perpetrated the deed by means of pokers, a swordstick, and a horse pistol.

A Mr Dawson, who was passing, about 9.00pm, heard loud noises, but thought it to be rough company, and took no more notice.

The Leeds Mercury of the day before had carried a similar account, of which the following is an extract:

"The old man, though mortally wounded, was still sensible, and enabled to give a brief account of the affair. He said that, during his son's absence, five Irishmen entered the house and, after compelling him to disclose where he kept his money, they attacked him, when, it is thought, at this moment his son returned home, and also became the victim of the bloodthirsty ruffians."

A week later, on April 14th, the Manchester Courier followed up the story:

On Saturday an inquest on the two Bradburys who were murdered in their cottage (sic) at Greenfield on the night of Monday week, was held at the King William IV public house, at Roadend, near Uppermill, before Michael Stokes, junior, coroner for the Agbrigg Division, and a respectable jury... who examined the following witnesses.

Mary Winterbottom, aged about 12 years, who said she had gone an errand for her mother, to get some barm for baking, from her grandfather Bradbury. She went straight in because the door was only on the latch, never locked; and in the first room she saw a man lying on the floor bleeding, and blood all around. No, she
72

did not know it was her uncle Tom; and the dog, Laddie, was standing over him, and would not let her near. She then ran down the road to the Whiteheads, who lived near, at Binn Green.

James Whitehead, accompanied by his wife and another person, said they went up to the Bradburys' and found Thomas stretched on the floor, encircled by blood. He never spoke, but groaned. On going up the stairs, which were bloody, they found the old man in bed, dreadfully wounded, and not able to utter an intelligible sound, except to say, very blurred, "Pats. Pats," from which he inferred that some Irishmen had murdered them for the sake of a few articles, and a little money.

The stairs, walls, windows, and every part of the house, were plashed with blood.

He then fetched Mr Sam Heginbottom, surgeon, who happened to be at his, James Whitehead's, house, attending his sick daughter.

Mr Heginbottom testified that he found the still-bleeding victim, downstairs, to be the younger Bradbury. The head had swelled considerably; it was fractured. This could have been caused by a blow from the rear; and could have been caused by blows from pokers, a broken pistol (which was found with Tom's hair and blood still adhering) or, probably, from a shovel, or spade; a sword-stick had been used but it was hollow and light. The spade was dyed in blood. The largest wound in the head was four inches long.

Roadend and the King William the Fourth Inn. The inquest on William and Thomas Bradbury was held at this pub.

Pulsation had ceased; and he died about three o'clock that afternoon.

He found about two pounds of coagulated blood near the pantry door; and every portion of furniture more or less bloody.

The old man was half-dressed, lying on the bed, bleeding profusely from frightful wounds in various parts of his body. His words were inarticulate. He died at one o'clock on the Wednesday morning. In the house he had found the swordstick of beech, resembling a flute (and was so used by Tom) which he knew to be the property of the younger man.

Near the dwelling was also picked up a broken horse-pistol, which he produced, and which, from its numerous locks and screws, etc. would form a desperate weapon, and had undoubtedly been used as, already described, it had Tom's hair adhering.

Reuben Platt, the person who had said that he had seen the three Irishmen near the spot on the night of the murder now said that, after going to the Bradburys' and staying some time, he being acquainted with them, the younger Bradbury left the house with him, leaving the old man alone, between six and seven o'clock, Platt to go home, Tom on an errand. They had not gone far on the road when they met three men. Before coming up to them Tom said: 'There's three Irish. I don't like them and leave my father at home yonder.' One of the Irishmen asked, How far to Holmfirth? Tom talked with him as if he knew him. The others skulked, and one of them turned his back on them. Tom afterwards said that he thought that the one who turned his back was the one who had stolen his stockings. He also expressed a wish to know what the fellows were after. He (witness) and Tom hung around a while pretending to measure some stones, and so saw the men well on their way past the inn. Tom then said, "Let's go," so they passed forward to the shop at Roadend, the place where Tom had come to buy the household articles, some mile and a half from the Bradburys'. The witness said he parted from Bradbury here, and went home. One of the men wore a torn shabby hat, blue slop and darkish-coloured cotton trousers; a second had light-coloured trousers, half boots, and a shabby black coat, and a torn hat; the third had an olive-coloured fustian velveteen jacket, with broad laps, and a rim round the buttons.

An Irishman named Charles Mullins, who was apprehended at Delph (a very few miles from Greenfield), on suspicion was brought before the coroner. A constable, Waterhouse, who had been despatched to Leeds to ascertain whether the account the prisoner gave of himself was correct, said he found it all to be true. The accused answered questions relative to where he had been so satisfactorily that he was immediately discharged.

A verdict of 'Wilful Murder against some person, or persons at present unknown' was returned. A reward of £100 is offered."

On the same day a paragraph in the Manchester Courier relating to the Petty Sessions read:

"Mr Hudson, constable of Rotherham, accompanied by one of Huddersfield's constables, appeared, to relate the particulars of apprehension of two men at Rotherham about 11 o'clock on Monday, suspected as two of the villains who murdered the Bradburys. The two men were taken, while applying for relief at the vagrants' office, Rotherham, in consequence of their dress corresponding to that described by Reuben Platt." One, William Jarvis, was wearing "a shabby fustian jacket, with broad laps." The other's dress did not correspond so well but there were some similarities. Both men refused to tell where they had been on the fatal night, but these had neither bundles, nor bruises on their faces or hands. They were detained pending further enquiries and there was no further report of them.

However, on April 21st the Manchester Courier reported two further suspects:

"Two persons bearing the name Bradbury, but no relation to the deceased, and commonly called 'Red Tom Bredburys', were apprehended at Huddersfield, on Monday, on suspicion of being concerned in the recent Saddleworth murders, under the following circumstances.

Both were well known as poachers; and a short time previously had been charged with pursuing game on the Greenfield plantations on information by Thomas Bradbury, and were bound over, from Saddleworth, to appear at Pontefract Quarter Sessions, these to commence on the day after the murder... and there the defendants appeared, claiming an acquittal, as Thomas Bradbury was unable to appear against them.

The magistrates, who had not yet heard of the horrid deed, were surprised at this information, which awakened suspicion, and the prisoners, who reside near Huddersfield, were taken into custody on the Monday, to appear before the magistrates of that town on that day."

These were Jamie Bradbury, better known as "Red Tom", and his son Joe. Jamie was said to have boasted that Tom o' Bill's o' Jack's would not appear against him at the sessions, and he was correct in claiming acquittal, as the prosecution could not proceed in Thomas Bradbury's absence. It was known that the two "Red Toms" had called at the New Inn (now the Church Inn) near Saddleworth Church, and could have learned there, from Reuben Platt, that the old man Bradbury would be alone in his inn. As they lived in Holmfirth, they would have to pass the inn on their way home.

There was little upon which to build a prosecution case; and the evidence of Jamie's daughter Matty that her father and brother would not have had time to call anywhere between leaving the New Inn and arriving home seems to have been accepted as an alibi. The phrase of the verdict, "some person or persons unknown," remains valid to this day.

Chapter 14

The examination of the evidence in the gossip of the villagers of Saddleworth, and their unofficial verdicts, differed from the official and reported version.

Three beshawled women, backs forming a compact triangle, shawls drawn, as was the way, half across the face, conferred in voices low and sibilant... "What did Reuben Platt want to go all that way round by Roadend wi' Tom o' Bill's? It put thri', four miles on his walk home. He could have crossed low to Dick Hill and ta'en a mile or so."

"Maybe so; but he could just have been biding Tom's company; few could get on wi' Tom, Reuben better than most."

"Doctor said, like, that the old fellow said 'Pats' when he were asked who'd hurt him. But doctor werna sure; old Bill's mouth were all mashed, jaw and all. Could ha' been 'Platt'."

"Give o'er, Sair Ellen. Old Bill would ne'er say 'Platt' for Reuben. Ne'er used his last name in his life; not the way round here. No, he would ha' said 'Reuben'."

"Have you thought," the third voice put in, "that he might ha' been saying 'Platters'?"

"Well, for sure they've no call for liking Tom Bradbury. Gave them a dog's life."

"And the gypsy lot moved on after the killing; just after."

"You can't make much to that. They always do, beginning of April. Known for it. Summer fairs, further south."

"Taproom lawyers" were arguing at the King William IV Inn, Roadend: "If tha'st so much to say, why didna speak at the Inquest? Tha knows thy way here, all right."

"Oh, aye! And get a bloody good thumping from Jamie Bradbury? Tha knows as well as I do o' his boasting, before eight o'clock o' the morn o' Tuesday."

"Aye. He'd have to leave bright and early to show up at the Sessions at Ponty that morn. But there he was, in a pub at Meltham, boasting that Tom o' Bill's would not speak against him that day, 'being in hell by now'. That's what they say he said."

"Were that e'er sworn to, I wonder? When Jamie Bradbury reaches Ponty - and all them miles, he must have had a lift - the news o' the murder were through. And maybe Jamie had heard, say, a whisper from a constable, opening his mouth too much."

"Maybe! Maybe! Maybe! And how had the news got to him at Meltham? A bloody talking pigeon?"

"Maybe he was just reckoning-on, like, that Tom o' Bill's were afeard on him. He been bragging o' that not long gone, up at the 'New'. Maybe that's all he meant."

"More bloody 'maybe's. Enough to stuff a duck."

Three men sat, one day warm for late April, on a drystone wall, out on the moors at Binn Green. Two wore round caps, peaks flat to the forehead, one a battered stove-pipe hat. The first 'cappie' was musing aloud: "Reuben brought talk on himself. Kept on about Tom o' Bill's being not easy in his mind about his old father. Naught o' the sort. Cared for the old fellow all right, as well as Tom were able, I reckon - sour sod - but he never moithered about him. Had no need to. No, it seems Reuben had to keep going on about them three Irishmen. But they would be on their way long before nightfall."

76

"I reckon Reuben were let off pretty lightly by yon crowner," agreed his friend in the stove-pipe hat. "All these things folks have asked each other about here were never asked by yon. Never found out for sure what Reuben Platt did after he left Tom o' Bill's, down yon at Roadend. They say he could ha' gone to the 'New'. They say he could ha' told the Red Tom Bradburys this, that and t'other. Always 'they' say; ne'er 'they' swore to it, before crowner."

"Aye, tha'rt right there," said the third of the party. "Didst know there were reckoned over thirty thousand folk come out here, noseying? Thirty thousand: afoot; ponyback; horseback some; all maks o' carts and lorry-flats. Lanes and roads were full. Eight thousand at burying and yet it 'pears to me there were damn little real talk in all that clatter and clutter."

(Stove-pipe hat) "Right again. Minds me, biggest bloody tattle-tale anywhere foot o' these moors has had naught to say, not e'en shown hisself, like."

(First cappie) "Eli o' John's, tha means?"

"Aye. A right know-all that, creeping round backs o' folks' houses. He could tell anybody what time they went out to t'closet. But come to think on't, he were noan seen around that much a week or two previous, like. He could be seen around, whiles, wi' Tom o' Bill's. Funny pair o' boots they two made together. Dead opposite o' one another."

"Could be that nobody would put up wi' Eli; so Tom, awkward bugger, would," suggested the second 'cappie'.

"More to it than that, to my mind." (Stove-pipe hat again.) "Eli knew every bugger's business. He knew who was poaching, and where and when they were doing it. As well - makes you laugh, don't it? - he would tell Tom when he could go poaching. Best of all at it, Tom. Good shot, too; better e'en than the Red Toms, who were good enough, by God! Double-riled 'em, see? They'd have had his guts out, sure, and laughed at 'em."

The second 'cappie' nodded: "But mention o' Eli minds me o' something else. What if old Bill said 'Platters', as they say?"

"Aye, funny thing, that." (First 'cappie') "Eli did· deal wi' them. Home made whiskey. Damn awful. Rot your clogs. Happen he'd been tattling about the old fellow's brass."

"No telling that; though he's generally more to say than most, he's had naught to say about this."

The stove-pipe hat had been thinking. Now he said reflectively, "Ne'er seen for some time. Bit o' talk about him then. Odd times seen wi' that big fellow, not o' these parts. A red silk to his throat, like a wrestler."

"Derbyshire spoken, they say," agreed the second 'cappie', "though who's to tell for sure, i' these parts? Pedlar-man too, they say, though I ne'er saw him wi' a tray. Not that I saw him more than two-three times, and I'm around as much as most."

(First 'cappie', musing): "Yon Platters had as much against Tom o' Bill's as any. Claimed rent from them, reckoning as land were his. Like a lot more round these parts. You know, when the Enclosures were baulked and land declared free, folks got around to claiming that they stood on, and a bloody sight more as well. Tom were counting from Bill's o' Jack's right up to Wessenden Head, and that's a mile or two."

"And he could be bloody rough, could Tom." (Second 'cappie'.) "E'en he asked pay, they say, for rushes and withies they gathered for their brushes and besoms."

"Aye. Tom were dead likely to come up to a mauling, some time. Hated by most everybody who used that road. Those who owned the dogs he poisoned. And wenches, and their lads."

"Well, if he did marlock around wi' the platter wenches, then he sought trouble, bad trouble."

"And that he got - but who gave it to him?"

"That we don't know, nor likely to. All those thousands been here, and so little said as means aught."

This gave the stove-pipe hat an opening: "Not a word, if you weigh it up right, to put against the word o' Matty Bradbury, Jamie's lass."

The first 'cappie' nodded: "Aye! Got her laces fastened, 'as Matty. All the brains there, I reckon."

"Here's what I mean. No talk getting around o' Matty washing her father's coat that night. That's well known here; but not to crowner. And there's summat else, and Matty's long head behind it, I reckon. Jamie's ne'er been since in a pub from that day to this. One time, the only time he werna in a pub were when he were walking from one to another. Might ha' spilt summat along with his ale."

"Matty would see to that," agreed his friend. "And any road, she'd be fain to do Tom Bradbury a bad service in any way. Fond enough o' Tom at one time. He were ale-taken and bragging one night in the taproom that she'd bared her arse for him once, standing in the snow."

"Just the sort o' rotten bloody thing Tom Bradbury would tell of a lass," put in the second 'cappie'. "He's shamed plenty, hurt more; and there'd be many a dry eye when they put Tom down."

(First 'cappie'): "Well, it's all argy-bargy, round and round. We canna make sense of it. I doubt anybody e'er will."

"Unless somebody can riddle out that letter. Read it us again, Fred," and 'Stovepipe' obligingly took from his pocket a much-folded, much-worn newspaper as he said musingly, "Funny he should know name, even first name, o' Deputy-Constable Lavender of Saddleworth, straight the day after." And he read again the letter, dated Huddersfield, April 3rd. (The original had been sent by Deputy-Constable Lavender to the Manchester Courier and seems to have been the basis of their report, since it contained the details of the bloodied bodies and the descriptions of the Irishmen.) " 'It is supposed they had gone towards Oldham or Manchester, and are probably escaping to Ireland. I consider information to you as the best course to adopt for their detection, and am respectfully, Your obedient servant. Thomas Smith.' And
78

there you are, Bob," said 'Stovepipe'. "Naught new, is there?"

"Don't try to be bloody clever, 'cause tha can read," retorted the second 'cappie'. "I say again, as I've said afore, that it reads to me like somebody pointing elsewhere so nobody should point at him."

The first 'cappie' agreed. "What makes it ring like a cracked bell, e'en more so now, is: why didna Mr Thomas Bloody Smith turn up at the Inquest?"

"Funny thing," opined 'Stovepipe' reflectively, "if he hadna been in it, the one who could ha' written a letter such, and sometimes did for folk, were Tom Bradbury hisself."

"Yes. He were a good scholard they say - our Ethel for one." (This from the second 'cappie'.) "He must ha' changed, for he were a quiet-spoken lad, they say, free as a lord wi' money or aught that he had. Naught but friendly wi' lasses; more particular, like, about keeping i' trim for his fighting."

"Well, by God, he changed i' that!"

(Stovepipe): "So we get no nearer and I'm going home. Half of us half know; a few o' t'others full know. But, so far as them who come rootling i' these lanes, they don't know, and ne'er will i' this world."

The second 'cappie' held up a finger: "Maybe so, but I've one last word. Here's a fight goes on half o' th'night, you might say, all o'er th'house - and even the walls had been bashed and cut. Now Tom Bradbury were best feighter e'er to come out o' these parts, say what else tha will against him. Yet has anybody round here shown so much as a cut, or a blackening o' th'face? And, by God, Tom Bradbury's blacked enough!"

"So then?"

"So then this. The only ones showing marks are Bill and Tom Bradbury."

The first 'cappie' looked sceptical. "Thou art saying what's been said a time or two in the village: 'They fought each other; to a standstill; to killing.' Tha tells me that, and one o'er eighty? That's just bloody daft!"

"Is it? Happen they fought so far; then were finished off."

"Aye, it is daft; and that dafter still." 'Stovepipe', by now bored with the discussion he had started, stood up decisively. "And now, by God, I **am** going home - after that!"

****

Postscript

Perhaps the final word should be left to Kenneth Hirst, who wrote an article which appeared in the Oldham Evening Chronicle on August 31st 1978.

NEW EVIDENCE IN MOORLAND MURDER MYSTERY

For almost a century and a half the brutal Bill's o' Jack's murders have defied detection.

On the night of April 2, 1832, 84-year-old William Bradbury, landlord of the Moorcock Inn on the Holmfirth road out of Greenfield, and his 46-year-old gamekeeper son, Tom, were savagely done to death.

There have been many theories about the crime, but the only certainty about it is that the murderer went to his grave unpunished.

But the latest number of the Saddleworth Historical Society's Bulletin raises the whole affair again with an article by Neil Barrow incorporating hitherto unconsidered evidence.

Briefly, the old man was found dying upstairs, and his son downstairs. The old man was less severely injured and lived longer, even being able to mutter a word or two. His son, an active, muscular chap who stood six feet and half an inch, never spoke a word after he was found, and died first.

Both had been brutally and bloodily battered, and the inside of the inn bore witness to a fierce struggle.

Theories about the identity of the murderer fall neatly into two categories. Either it was someone who knew the Bradburys, and perhaps bore them a grudge; or it was a stranger whose motive might have been robbery.

Before he died, the old man was heard to mutter repeatedly a word which sounded like "Pats". This could be interpreted as "Platt" meaning Reuben Platt, who had been in the inn that evening, and had walked with Tom Bradbury down to Greenfield, where Tom o' Bill's, as he was known, was doing some shopping.

Reuben Platt gave evidence at the inquest, and came under suspicion in some eyes, but he was never a convincing suspect.

The other category of suspect hangs on a different interpretation of the word "Pats". This was widely taken to refer to Irish gypsies who collected broom on the moors to make into brushes, and who were often in conflict with the Bradburys over their right to be on the moors.

Or "Pats" could be taken to mean navvies who lived in huts at Greenfield and who, at the time, were working on the turnpike to Holmfirth.

But the prime suspect was a Jamie Bradbury (no relation to the victims), who was due at Pontefract the following day to answer a charge of poaching. He was heard to boast that Tom o' Bill's would never appear at Pontefract Court to bear witness against him.

Jamie and his son Joe were arrested and examined at Huddersfield, but were released for lack of evidence.

And so the case has rested for nearly a century and a half. There have been many rumours of confessions, but none with any substance.

What the article in the current issue of the Bulletin does is to produce a letter recently rediscovered in an issue of the Huddersfield Examiner dated March 5, 1853, telling of a confession - and that letter itself was published 21 years after the event. It reads:

"Mr Whitehead a sheep farmer, about 169 miles from Melbourne, Australia, says,... I went into a public house at Port Fary. Whilst there, a man came into my room and said, 'I know you, and knew your uncles. There was a murder committed in Saddleworth; was it ever found out?' Mr W said he believed not.

The man then said, 'It was a young man hawking tape in a basket who murdered Bill and Tom o' Jack's. I at the time was working at repairing the canal at Saddleworth as an excavator, and the man, soon after the murder of Bill and Tom o' Jack's, went to Leicester and committed a robbery upon a drover, for which crime he was transported to Sydney. Since he came here he has committed a murder for which he was hung in Hobart Town.

'Previous to being executed he confessed to me that he had murdered Bill and Tom Bradbury of Greenfield, but that he had no intention to kill anyone, but to rob the house, and for that purpose sent the old man upstairs, but soon coming down again he struck him on the head, which disabled him.

'The hawker said he was put off robbing the house by Tom coming in. Previous to his return, old Bill crawled upstairs. The tape-hawker was searching the drawers but found nothing.

'Whilst doing this, Tom came, when the man was going away. Seeing Tom come, he turned back, and as he entered the door, knocked him down with a fire poker.'

The man who made this statement to Mr Whitehead is now carrying on the business of wool-carrier, with a bullock dray at Port Fary, and states that he had been a mate of the tape-hawker who had confessed to him the crime which has so long and so mysteriously baffled all the attempts made to discover its perpetrators."

That this letter to the Huddersfield Examiner should have lain unheeded in the newspaper's files for well over a century serves only to underline what all historians know, that all newspaper files contain millions of words of history accessible only to those who know a date to turn up. The article in the Bulletin credits Terence Wyke with its discovery.

It also deals with another aspect of the double murder which is always well to the forefront when the crime is being discussed, namely the unpopularity of William and Tom Bradbury, and quotes two sources of evidence.

Joseph Thornton, writing some time in the second half of the 18th century, comments:

"The fact was that there were too many unwilling witnesses some of whom could have hanged the culprit on their own evidence. Many declined to come forward with substantial facts on account of the unfriendly behaviour of the Bradburys towards those who had to travel on the road from Greenfield to Holmfirth.

"The gamekeeper was a terror to pedestrians as well as to the poacher... Statements have since been made that if the tragedy had not taken place on the above date, it would have taken place shortly afterwards."

And to reinforce this point of view, the article quotes a diary being kept by George Shaw of St Chad's, who was 19 at the time of the entry:

"August 12, 1829... there have been four or five dogs poisoned about Bill o' Jack's with small pieces of muffin which had been evidently scattered about on purpose for mischief, and which on being examined were found to contain leather buttons. It is supposed that Tom o' Bill's has been the author of this diabolical action in revenge for being fined for shooting last year."

Neil Barrow, the author of the article, comments: "Thus this new evidence provides a confession and a motive, but as they are irreconcilable they add further to the mystery."

It seems to me, however, that the story of how the murder took place fits the facts remarkably well.

It answers such questions as how one man could have overcome two, one of whom was a muscular six-footer. And it explains why one was found upstairs and one was found downstairs.

It explains too, how - an unusual circumstance - no death-bed confession had turned up during the lifetime of people who remembered the tragedy. And if the evidence of Joseph Thornton and George Shaw is to be taken into account it makes sense if you regard the two testimonials not so much as a motive for the murder as a reason why the murderer was never brought to book.

It would have been useful to know who was the writer of the letter to the Examiner and whether there had been any follow-up afterwards, but perhaps that is a matter for further research.

****